APRIL 2004

Pollution Probe is pleased to present this Primer on Climate Change and Human Health. The primer describes the potential effects that a warmer and more variable climate can have on our health. It discusses the climate change impacts that are expected to occur across Canada, as well as some of the actions being taken by various levels of government to reduce greenhouse gas emissions and to help Canadians adapt to a changing climate. Helpful tips are given on what you can do to reduce emissions of greenhouse gases and ways in which you can protect yourself from harmful effects.

The primer can also be read in conjunction with Pollution Probe's complementary primers on smog, acid rain, the technologies of renewable energy, drinking water, mercury and the soon-to-be released source water protection primer. Together, these primers, and others that will be prepared on topics of interest, provide a broad educational base upon which to understand the environmental issues that we face today, as well as the solutions that will need to be implemented.

Your comments on this primer are welcome. We also appreciate feedback on the usefulness of this primer to you and others. This primer can be downloaded free-of-charge from our website (www.pollutionprobe.org/Publications/Primers.htm). Printed copies are also available for a small fee to cover printing and distribution costs.

K. B. Ogilvie

Ken Ogilvie
Executive Director

ACKNOWLEDGEMENTS

Pollution Probe gratefully acknowledges the funding support and technical review of the *Primer on Climate Change and Human Health* by the following organizations:

GOVERNMENT OF CANADA — CLIMATE CHANGE ACTION FUND   Canada

DUPONT CANADA

ENBRIDGE GAS DISTRIBUTION

ONTARIO FORESTRY ASSOCIATION

ONTARIO POWER GENERATION INC.

We also thank the following individuals for providing technical information and/or comments on the Primer: **Peter Berry, Rob Cross, Angus Fergusson, Gwen Goodier, Henry Hengeveld, Pam Kertland, Joan Klaassen, Abdel Maarouf, Kim Perrotta, Tariq Piracha, Dieter Riedel, Andrew Wahba** and **Fiona Warren.**

Pollution Probe is solely responsible for the contents of this publication.

This publication was researched and written for Pollution Probe by **Olivia Nugent** and edited by **Randee Holmes.** We appreciate the work of staff members **Ken Ogilvie, Quentin Chiotti, Elizabeth Everhardus** and **Krista Friesen.**

Special thanks are given to **Shauna Rae** for design and layout of the Primer.

ISBN 0-919764-55-X

TABLE OF CONTENTS

Introduction to Climate Change

There is international scientific agreement that the world is getting warmer. By examining climate records, scientists have determined that the temperature of the air at the Earth's surface has warmed by approximately 0.6°C since the late 19th century (see Figure 1-1). Evidence from tree rings, tropical corals and Greenland ice cores indicates that, at least for the Northern Hemisphere, the 20th century was the warmest of the past 1,000 years, with the 1990s being the warmest decade of the millennium. Furthermore, it's getting ever warmer – most experts agree that average global temperatures will rise by 1.4°C to 5.8°C over the next century.

Figure 1-1

Global Temperature Changes
(1860-2002) (Relative to 1961–1990 average temperature)

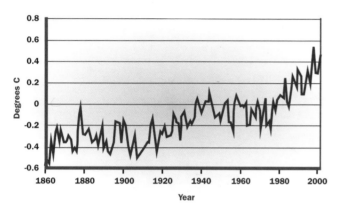

Source: Environment Canada. 2002. *Science and Impacts of Climate Change.*

In Canada, climate change would mean an increase in annual mean temperatures in some regions of more than 5°C. Such abrupt temperature changes would cause a broad range of impacts. Glaciers and polar ice packs would shrink. Sea levels would rise, flooding coastal areas. Higher maximum temperatures would mean more heat waves. Droughts and wildfires would occur more often.

Relatively small changes in average temperatures can have huge consequences. During the last Ice Age, about 20,000 years ago, average temperatures were only 5°C cooler than they are today, but most of Canada was covered by several kilometres of ice.

Climate change is more than just a global warming trend. Increasing temperatures will also lead to changes in many aspects of weather, such as wind patterns, the amount and type of precipitation, and the severity and frequency of extreme weather events. With climate influencing so much in our lives – from where we live to what we wear, from what we eat to our choice of lifestyle – any change could have far-reaching health, environmental, social and economic consequences.

This primer deals with the health consequences of climate change and what we can do to protect ourselves. Canadians have long adapted to the current climate, but past success is no guarantee that we will be able to cope with the health impacts that may occur as a result of climate change. This primer also discusses the climate change impacts that are being projected across Canada and the actions being taken by various levels of government to reduce greenhouse gas emissions and to help Canadians adapt. As well, helpful tips are given on what you can do to reduce your personal emissions of the greenhouse gases that are causing climate change.

But first, the key to understanding climate change is to understand the global climate system and how it works.

The Global Climate System

On a global scale, climate is largely regulated by how much energy the Earth receives from the sun and how much energy it releases back to space. The global climate is also affected by other flows of energy within the climate system itself. These energy flows are regulated by the atmosphere (which provides gases, aerosols, clouds and winds), the oceans (which help to distribute heat through currents), precipitation (in the form of rain, snow or ice), water (in the form of lakes and rivers) and land (which reflects or absorbs energy from the sun). Changes to any of these elements can affect the balance of the entire system, causing the climate to change. A good example of this is the weather phenomenon known as El Niño. Above-average Pacific Ocean water temperatures have affected the patterns of tropical rainfall from Indonesia all the way to the west coast of South America, a distance roughly equal to half of the world's circumference. These changes in tropical rainfall have, in turn, affected weather patterns around the globe.

The Natural Greenhouse Effect

Energy from the sun drives the Earth's climate. As the sun's energy reaches the Earth's surface, some of it is reflected back and some of it is absorbed. The absorbed energy warms the Earth. This heat is then radiated back out towards space as infrared energy. Certain chemical compounds in the Earth's atmosphere act as "greenhouse gases," absorbing the radiated infrared energy and thereby trapping some of the heat in the atmosphere.

BOX 1-1

What's the Difference Between Climate and Weather?

Weather is the condition of various elements of the atmosphere at a particular place and time. It is what is happening outside at a certain moment. A thunderstorm or blizzard would be classified as "weather." In most places, weather can change from hour-to-hour, day-to-day and season-to-season. Climate is what you get when you average the weather over a long period of time (usually 30 years, sometimes more) and when you look at how the weather varies around these averages. For example, a place that doesn't get much rain over many years would be described as having a dry climate. A place where it stays cold for most of the year would be described as having a cold climate.

Figure 1-2

The Greenhouse Effect

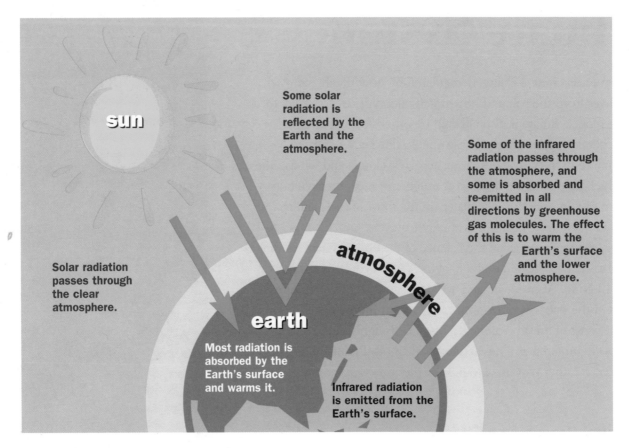

Some solar radiation is reflected by the Earth and the atmosphere.

Some of the infrared radiation passes through the atmosphere, and some is absorbed and re-emitted in all directions by greenhouse gas molecules. The effect of this is to warm the Earth's surface and the lower atmosphere.

Solar radiation passes through the clear atmosphere.

Most radiation is absorbed by the Earth's surface and warms it.

Infrared radiation is emitted from the Earth's surface.

Source: US Global Change Research Program. www.usgcrp.gov.

The greenhouse gases radiate this energy in all directions, including back to the Earth again (Figure 1-2). This energy is used in a number of processes, including heating the ground surface, melting ice and snow, evaporating water, and plant photosynthesis. Most importantly this energy remains trapped within the climate system, warming the Earth's surface to an average of 14°C. This phenomenon, called the "natural greenhouse effect," keeps the Earth in a temperature range that allows life to thrive. Without it, the sun's heat would escape and the average temperature of the Earth would drop to –19°C.

CHAPTER ONE: **INTRODUCTION TO CLIMATE CHANGE**

To understand how the natural greenhouse effect can impact the climate of a planet, Venus and Mars can be used as examples. Venus has a very thick atmosphere (approximately 90 times denser than Earth's atmosphere). Much of this – 96 per cent – is made up of carbon dioxide (CO_2). This thick atmosphere does not allow much heat to escape to space. It is also closer to the sun than is Earth. As a result, the planet has an average surface temperature of about 475°C. Mars, on the other hand, has a very thin atmosphere of greenhouse gases (although 95 per cent CO_2, it has less than one per cent of the density of Earth's atmosphere). This thin atmosphere means that it cannot retain energy from the sun, resulting in only a small greenhouse effect on the planet. Mars is also further away from the sun than is Earth. Hence, its surface temperature is on average about –60°C.

On Earth, the careful balance of greenhouse gases has created ideal conditions in which humans, animals and plants can thrive.

The Enhanced Greenhouse Effect

Human activities can disrupt the balance of the global climate system. Any changes in atmospheric greenhouse gas concentrations will affect the amount of energy stored in the atmosphere. For example, when the amount of carbon dioxide (CO_2) – a major greenhouse gas – is increased, more heat is trapped in the atmosphere. This "enhanced greenhouse effect" causes the Earth's surface temperature to rise. Since the beginning of the industrial revolution (about 1750 AD), the concentration of all the major greenhouse gases has increased in the atmosphere, thereby helping to bring about the changes in climate that the world is currently experiencing.

BOX 1-2

Climate Change and Global Warming are not the Same Thing

The terms "global warming" and "climate change" are often used to describe the same phenomenon. In actuality they are distinguishable as cause and effect, or problem and consequence. **Global warming** refers only to the increase in the temperature of the Earth's lower atmosphere as a result of the enhanced greenhouse effect. The resulting impacts of this temperature increase — changes in many aspects of weather — are what we refer to as **climate change**. This includes shifts in wind patterns and the amount and type of precipitation, which in turn influence the types and frequency of severe weather events that may be expected to occur in an area. Thus, we are experiencing climate change as a result of global warming. The term **climate variability** is used to describe the way climate varies around average climate conditions, on time scales from seasons and years to decades and longer. Much of climate variability is caused by natural oscillations in ocean currents and atmospheric pressure patterns. However, climate change caused by humans can also affect climate variability.

It is important to note that the planet underwent several climatic shifts prior to the industrial revolution. For example, from 1000–1300 AD, there was a period of relatively mild climate called the "Medieval Warm Period" when temperatures in the northern hemisphere were believed to be at least 0.8°C warmer than today. A few centuries later, between 1450 and 1850 AD during what is termed the "Little Ice Age," global temperatures were between 1.0 and 2.0°C cooler than today. Scientists believe these two climatic shifts were caused by natural fluctuations in the sun's radiation. Increased volcanic activity, which can interfere with the amount of energy absorbed at the Earth's surface, may also have contributed to the cooling temperatures of the Little Ice Age.

The Main Greenhouse Gases

Many gases in the atmosphere exhibit "greenhouse" properties. These include those occurring naturally in the atmosphere, such as CO_2, methane, nitrous oxide and water vapour, as well as gases produced from human activities and referred to as halocarbons (i.e., chlorofluorocarbons (CFCs), hydrofluorocarbons (HFCs), perfluorocarbons (PFCs) and sulfur hexafluoride (SF_6)).

The ability of a greenhouse gas to warm the Earth depends on its capacity to absorb heat (known as the "global warming potential" or GWP), as well as on its atmospheric lifetime when released into the atmosphere. GWP is the heat trapping potential per molecule of the gas compared to a molecule of CO_2 (which has a GWP of 1.0) over a 100-year timeframe. For example, methane has a GWP of 23, which means that over 100 years each molecule of methane traps heat 23 times more effectively than CO_2. The atmospheric lifetime of a greenhouse gas refers to the length of time that a gas remains in the atmosphere and, hence, its ability to influence climate. Some gases have relatively short atmospheric lifetimes (e.g., 12 years for methane (CH_4)), while others (e.g., halocarbons) remain in the atmosphere and continue to absorb the sun's heat for hundreds or even thousands of years. Table 1-1 compares the atmospheric lifetimes and the GWPs of the major greenhouse gases.

TABLE 1-1: **Greenhouse Gas Concentrations, Atmospheric Lifetimes and Global Warming Potentials**

GAS	OBSERVED ATMOSPHERIC CONCENTRATION CHANGES	ATMOSPHERIC LIFETIME (YEARS)	GLOBAL WARMING POTENTIAL (GWP)
CARBON DIOXIDE (CO_2)	There has been a 31 per cent increase in atmospheric concentration of CO_2 from 280 parts per million (ppm) in 1750 to 368 ppm* in the year 2000. *368 ppm of CO_2 means that, for every million litres of gases in the air, 368 of them are CO_2.	The atmospheric lifetime of CO_2 is usually given as 150 years; however this can fluctuate due to the variable absorption and emission rates from forests, living organisms and the oceans.	1.0
METHANE (CH_4)	There has been a 151 per cent increase in atmospheric concentration of CH_4, from 700 parts per billion (ppb) in the year 1750 to 1,750 ppb* in the year 2000. *1,750 ppb of CH_4 means that for every billion litres of gases in the air, 1,750 of them are CH_4.	12	Although methane is much less abundant than CO_2 in the Earth's atmosphere, gram for gram it has 23 times the heat-trapping effect.
NITROUS OXIDES (N_2O)	There has been a 17.5 per cent increase in atmospheric concentration of N_2O, from 270 ppb in 1750 to 316 ppb in the year 2000.	114	In contrast to CO_2, N_2O is emitted into the atmosphere in small quantities. However, one gram of N_2O can absorb about 300 times more energy than can one gram of CO_2. Therefore, although N_2O occurs in very low concentrations, its tremendous heat-trapping ability means that it has substantial climate influence.
HALOCARBONS (CFCs, HCFCs, HFCs, PFCs AND SF_6)	There has been an increase in atmospheric concentrations of HCFCs from 0 parts per trillion (ppt) in 1750 to as much as 132 ppt* (for HCFC-22) in 1999. CFCs have increased from 0 ppt in 1750 to as much as 533 ppt (for CFC-12) in the year 2000. *132 ppt of HCFCs means that for every trillion litres of gases in the air, 132 of them are HCFCs.	The range of atmospheric lifetimes for halocarbons is enormous, from 0.3 years to more than 50,000 years.	CFCs, HCFCs: 120–14,000 GWP HFCs: 12–12,000 GWP PFCs: 5,700–11,900 GWP SF_6: 22,200 GWP

Sources of Greenhouse Gases

In January 2001, the Intergovernmental Panel on Climate Change (IPCC), made up of top scientists from around the world, concluded that "there is new and stronger evidence that most of the warming observed over the last 50 years is attributable to human activity." Humans are adding more and more greenhouse gases to the atmosphere, mainly through the burning or "combustion" of fossil fuels (i.e., petroleum, natural gas and coal) to transport people and goods, heat and cool buildings, generate electricity and operate industries. Agricultural activities and manufacturing processes are also significant sources of some gases (see Figure 1-3). In addition, changes in land cover and land use for agriculture, urbanization and road construction can affect the concentrations of greenhouse gases in the atmosphere. Land use change often involves the clearing of forests and vegetation (e.g., the tropical rainforests in South America). When these large swaths of vegetation are cleared, the area has considerably less capacity to absorb and store CO_2 through photosynthesis (the process by which green plants use energy from the sun to convert CO_2 into fuel for growth). In addition, if forests are removed by burning, the CO_2 stored in the tree wood is returned to the atmosphere.

Figure 1-3

Percentage of GHG Emissions by Sector for Canada (1998)

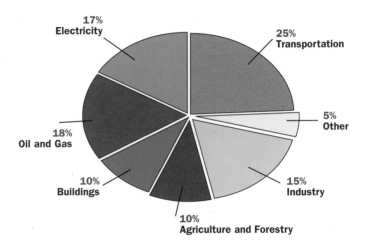

Source: Government of Canada. 2000. *Action Plan 2000 on Climate Change.*

There are also natural activities that add greenhouse gases to the atmosphere. For example, natural sources of CO_2 include the respiration of people, animals and plants, volcanic eruptions and gas emissions from the oceans (these vast water bodies are huge absorbers and storehouses of CO_2 and other gases). Together, these natural sources release about 550 billion tonnes of CO_2 each year, far outweighing the 30 billion tonnes released by human activity. While natural CO_2 removal processes, such as photosynthesis by plants, keep the large volume of natural releases in check, they cannot absorb the added emissions from human activity. Consequently, this gas is building up in the atmosphere (see Figure 1-4). Table 1-2 lists the major greenhouse gases and discusses their sources in more detail.

While international efforts are being made to reduce greenhouse gas emissions, these actions will not stop climate change from occurring before the end of this century, at which time CO_2 levels are projected to double (or possibly triple) from pre-industrial levels. Consequently, Canadians will have to learn to adapt to some degree of future climate change. However, by taking actions to reduce our greenhouse gas emissions today,

Canadians can help slow down the speed at which climate change will occur. Taking actions to cut back on greenhouse gas emissions will require reducing energy use. Such reductions will also have co-benefits for our health and for the environment, by improving local air quality and reducing the emissions that cause acid rain.

Figure 1-4

Atmospheric Build-up of CO_2 (1750–2000)

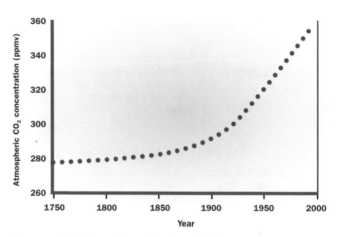

Source: ARIC, Atmosphere, Climate and Environment Information Programme.

TABLE 1-2: **Greenhouse Gases and Their Sources**

GAS	WHAT IT IS	WHERE IT COMES FROM
CARBON DIOXIDE (CO₂)	CO_2 is a colourless, odourless non-flammable gas. It is recycled through the atmosphere by the process of photosynthesis.	CO_2 is the most significant greenhouse gas released as a result of human activities. CO_2 is released to the atmosphere when carbon-containing waste, fossil fuels and wood are burned. CO_2 can also enter the air from the decay of plants, and from air exhaled by animals when they breathe. There are also small amounts of emissions from volcanoes, but much less than those produced by humans. Land use changes, such as clearing land for logging, ranching and agriculture, also lead to CO_2 emissions. Vegetation contains carbon that is released as CO_2 when the vegetation decays or burns.
METHANE (CH₄)	CH_4 is a colourless, odourless gas, and, in the ground, is a by-product of the geologic process that turns organic material into coal.	Methane is emitted during the production and transport of coal, natural gas and oil. Methane is also produced when vegetation is burned, digested or rotted in the absence of oxygen. Primary sources include wetlands, rice paddies, animal digestive processes and decaying garbage.
NITROUS OXIDES (N₂O)	There are several forms of nitrogen oxides that contribute to poor air quality and other problems, such as acid rain, but N_2O is the only one that is a significant greenhouse gas.	Natural processes occurring in soils and oceans are the primary natural sources of N_2O. Humans contribute to N_2O emissions through the use of nitrogen fertilizers, the production of nylon and the burning of organic material. The burning of fossil fuels also contributes a large portion of N_2O, particularly through vehicle use.
HALOCARBONS (CFCs, HCFCs, HFCs, PFCs AND SF₆)	Halocarbons are a family of chemicals that contain chlorine, fluorine or bromine. Chlorofluorocarbons (CFCs), hydrochlorofluorocarbons (HCFCs), hydrofluorocarbons (HFCs), perfluorocarbons (PFCs) and sulphur hexafluoride (SF_6) are all halocarbons. Halocarbons with chlorine present are responsible for damaging the stratospheric ozone layer (i.e., CFCs and HCFCs).	These powerful greenhouse gases are generated in a variety of industrial processes. A small amount of these gases is generated naturally through decaying organic matter and volcanic eruptions. Chlorofluorocarbons (CFCs) have been used in refrigeration and air conditioning, and as solvents. Likewise, HCFCs are used in refrigeration, aerosol propellants, foam manufacture and air conditioning. PFCs are emitted principally from aluminium production. Sulphur hexafluoride (SF_6) is emitted by the electric power industry in the production of circuit breakers, gas-insulated substations and switchgear.

TABLE 1-2: **Greenhouse Gases and Their Sources** *(continued)*

GAS	WHAT IT IS	WHERE IT COMES FROM
WATER VAPOUR (H$_2$O)	Water vapour comes from the evaporation of water, transpiration and natural respiration. The amount of water vapour stored in the atmosphere increases as the Earth's surface temperature rises.	Human activities do not directly add significant amounts of water vapour to the atmosphere. Indirectly, however, by causing temperatures to rise, human activity does cause increased water vapour to be released into the atmosphere. Warmer air itself contains more water vapour than does cooler air. It also causes more surface water to evaporate. Since water vapour is itself a greenhouse gas, rising global temperatures will be further enhanced by the increased amounts of water vapour in the atmosphere.

Climate Change and Human Health

I n a December 11th, 2003 press release, the World Health Organization stated that "there is growing evidence that changes in the global climate will have profound effects on the health and well-being of citizens in countries throughout the world" (see Box 2-1). These effects will be felt by humans by way of several different routes. Most directly, health will be affected through temperature extremes of heat or cold that could result in illness and death. As well, extreme weather events, such as more frequent and intense rainstorms and windstorms, hurricanes and tornadoes, could result in death, injury and other harmful effects.

Health Impacts of Climate Change

According to a 2003 report authored by the World Health Organization (WHO), the United Nations Environment Programme (UNEP) and the World Meteorological Organization (WMO), climate change is responsible for 2.4 per cent of all cases of diarrhea worldwide and for two per cent of all cases of malaria. Moreover, in the year 2000 an estimated 150,000 deaths were caused by climate change.

Source: World Health Organization. 2003. *Climate Change and Human Health — Risks and Responses.*

Climate change will also affect human health somewhat less directly by affecting the environment and ecosystems within which we live. These indirect effects will occur through insect- and rodent-transmitted diseases (e.g., West Nile virus fever; Lyme disease and Hantavirus Pulmonary Syndrome); increased smog and air pollution; waterborne and food-related illnesses (e.g., giardiasis, E. coli infection, and shellfish poisoning); and stronger UV radiation, which is a leading cause of skin cancer and cataracts. The time frame for the emergence of these health impacts can range from immediately (e.g., a storm-related injury), to weeks or months (e.g., an insect-transmitted infection), to years and decades (e.g., UV-related malignancies).

Some positive health effects may result from climate change as warmer winters could reduce cold-related deaths. However, the negative effects of climate change tend to far outweigh the positive effects. This primer deals primarily with the harmful, or potentially harmful, human health effects of climate change.

Temperature Extremes

Extreme temperature events, by definition, are rare and are usually associated with heat waves in the summer and cold spells in the winter. An extreme heat wave is a prolonged period of excessive daytime and night time heat, usually in association with high humidity and related to geographic location and time of year. In Canada, a heat wave is defined as three or more days of 32°C temperatures and beyond. With climate change, cold temperature extremes are expected to become less frequent, while heat waves will become more frequent. Record extremes in high temperatures are already occurring in some parts of the world,

the most recent being heat waves that took place across Europe in the summer of 2003 and to which the World Health Organization has attributed 20,000 deaths.

Health Effects

Heat can kill by pushing the human body beyond its capability to keep cool. Under warm conditions, the body's internal thermostat makes the skin produce perspiration that evaporates and cools the body. However, in extreme heat and high humidity, this cooling process is slowed and the body must work harder to maintain a normal temperature.

The clothed human body can handle most variations in weather, within certain limits. However, extreme changes in weather, such as heat waves, can cause adverse health effects, such as heat cramps, fainting, heat exhaustion and heatstroke. (Heat in combination with air pollution can also exacerbate respiratory and cardiovascular conditions. This relationship is discussed in more detail later in this chapter.)

BOX 2-2

How to Treat a Heat Emergency

Heat cramps: Heat cramps are muscular pains and spasms due to heavy exertion. Although heat cramps are the least severe of the heat-related ailments, they are often the first signal that the body is having trouble with the heat. Get the person to a cooler place and have him or her rest in a comfortable position. Lightly stretch the affected muscle and replenish fluids. Give a half glass of cool water every 15 minutes. Do not give liquids with alcohol or caffeine in them, as they can cause further dehydration, making conditions worse.

Heat exhaustion: Heat exhaustion typically occurs when people exercise heavily or work in a hot, humid place where body fluids are lost through heavy sweating. Blood flow to the skin increases, causing blood flow to vital organs to decrease. This results in a form of mild shock. If not treated, the victim's condition will worsen. Body temperature will keep rising and the victim may suffer a stroke. Get the person out of the heat and into a cooler place. Remove or loosen tight clothing and apply cool, wet cloths, such as towels or sheets. If the person is conscious, give cool water to drink. Make sure the person drinks slowly. Give a half glass of cool water every 15 minutes. Let the victim rest in a comfortable position, and watch carefully for changes in his or her condition.

BOX 2-2 — *continued*

How to Treat a Heat Emergency

Heat stroke: Heat stroke is a life-threatening situation. The victim's temperature control system, which produces sweating to cool the body, stops working. The body temperature can rise so high that brain damage and death may result if the body is not cooled quickly. Help is needed fast. Call 9-1-1 or your local emergency number. Move the person to a cooler place. Quickly cool the body. Immerse the victim in a cool bath, or wrap wet sheets around the body and fan it. Watch for signals of breathing problems. Keep the person lying down and continue to cool the body any way you can. If the victim refuses water or is vomiting, or if there are changes in the level of consciousness, do not give anything to eat or drink.

Source: The American Red Cross.

According to a study published by Environmental Health Perspectives, during periods of excessive heat emergency rooms report an overall increase in visits, specifically for the symptoms noted earlier. The study indicated that a rise in the heat index – which refers to the temperature the body feels when heat and humidity are combined – is followed by an increase in the number of deaths due to heat. In July 1995, a heat wave contributed to as many as 765 heat-related deaths in the Chicago area alone. A study that examined the relationship between weather and heat-related deaths in Toronto from 1979 to 1989 found that 14 per cent of the variability for all deaths in persons 0–65 years of age was related to weather conditions. Other studies have shown that cities have "temperature thresholds" that determine when the death rate begins to rise above normal. These thresholds can vary from city to city. For example, in cities where heat waves are rare, these thresholds are lower than in places where heat waves are more common. This is because if a population is not acclimatized to hotter temperatures then people will experience the effects of heat more severely. In Canada, Toronto has a higher temperature threshold (32°C), for example, than Montreal (29°C); this means that people in Montreal are at greater risk of experiencing adverse reactions to heat-related events when they occur.

The most common cause of death and the most serious illness directly related to heat is heatstroke, a condition in which the body temperature is greater than 40.6°C. Other causes of death related to heat waves include ischemic heart disease (a condition in which blood flow is restricted to the heart), diabetes, stroke, respiratory diseases and accidents. Acts of violence and homicide also appear to increase due to the stress and aggravation of intense temperatures.

The magnitude of these health effects is difficult to predict and depends on a variety of factors, such as suddenness of heat onset, city planning for heat emergencies, and regional heat tolerance. In temperate climate cities, heat waves that occur early in the summer may be deadlier than those that occur later, mainly because people have not had time to acclimatize to the heat and, therefore, are more sensitive to hot weather stresses. The duration of the heat wave is also a significant factor. According to the American Red Cross, studies show that a significant rise in heat-related illnesses happens when excessive heat lasts more than two days.

Who is at Risk?

When the body is exposed to extreme or prolonged heat, one of its cooling mechanisms is to increase surface blood circulation, which requires the heart to pump faster and harder. Thus, groups susceptible to heat include the elderly and people with weak hearts or cardiac diseases. Studies have found that the risk for heat-related death increases sharply with age. Women over 85 years of age are most at risk of heat-related mortality. Increases in hospital visits for cardiovascular diseases, and increases in deaths due to cardiovascular and respiratory diseases, have also been documented during heat waves, suggesting that heat exacerbates these conditions.

BOX 2-3

Urban Heat Island Effect

A heat phenomenon termed the "urban heat island effect" may intensify the excess heat situation in metropolitan areas. This effect occurs when natural vegetation, which has a cooling effect, is replaced by surfaces that absorb heat, such as building roofs, walls and pavement. This can make cities several degrees warmer than surrounding non-urban areas. In addition, the heat absorbed during the day is released during the night, keeping night time temperatures high, so people do not get a chance to cool off and recuperate before the next day's high temperatures. The severity of urban heat island effects varies from city to city and can be affected by certain factors. For example, in Toronto, the daytime heat island effects in the downtown core can sometimes be alleviated by the presence of lake breezes from nearby Lake Ontario.

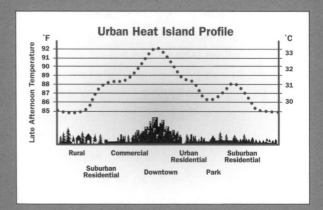

Like the elderly, young children are at high risk for heat-related illnesses. Both the very old and the very young tend to have more difficulty regulating body heat. In addition, they may be less able to move freely, resulting in less control over their situation.

Persons who are engaged in exercise or heavy work – particularly outdoor work – can suffer from dehydration if not drinking enough fluids. As well, since men tend to sweat more than women, they can become dehydrated more quickly, making them more susceptible to a heat-related illness.

Populations vulnerable to the impacts of excessive heat exposure include those with low or fixed incomes who may not have access to air conditioning, pools, or cool recreational areas. Many urban populations are more vulnerable than non-urban populations to heat stress because of the "urban heat island effect" (see Box 2-3). During a heat wave in St. Louis, Missouri, there were more deaths in the business and urban core areas than in other, cooler sections of the city. Finally, people taking medications or drugs that affect the body's ability to regulate heat are also at increased risk.

Extreme Weather

The term "extreme" usually refers to a departure from the norm. Thus, in terms of weather, "extreme" often refers to severe events, such as hurricanes, tornadoes, ice storms, storm surges, floods and drought. Weather becomes more extreme with climate change largely because warming speeds up the water cycle (the process by which water vapour rises into the atmosphere and condenses as precipitation). Warmer temperatures heat the Earth's surface, which leads to faster evaporation and hence more moisture in the atmosphere. Increased moisture in the air means more water vapour will condense as precipitation. Therefore, as more heat and moisture is put into the atmosphere, precipitation-driven events, such as storms, floods, hurricanes and tornadoes, will intensify in some parts of the world. Sea levels around the world will rise because increasing temperatures cause ocean seawater to expand as it warms (this "thermal expansion" is believed to have been a major influence on past changes in sea levels). Levels will also rise due to the melting of glaciers and ice caps, which will increase the volume of water in the world's oceans. This, in turn, will tend to lead to more storm surges along coastal regions.

Not all areas will become wetter. While the oceans become heated, so will the land. As a result, the land may become parched in some areas due to rapid evaporation of water from soils, lakes and reservoirs. Interior regions, such as the Canadian Prairies, will become drier, with more prolonged periods of drought. This parching of soil can also lead to secondary effects, such as the development of unstable winds, tornadoes and other powerful storms.

According to the World Meteorological Organization (WMO), record extremes in weather and climate events, such as droughts, tornadoes and high temperatures, continue to occur around the world. Recent scientific evidence indicates that, as global temperatures continue to warm due to climate change, the number and intensity of extreme events might increase. Over the past few years, Canada has seen an unusual number of these severe weather events, with traumatic results, such as the ice storm in Eastern Ontario and Western Quebec in 1998 (see Box 2-6), extensive flooding in the Saguenay region (1996) and southern Manitoba (1997), record accumulation of snow in Toronto and southern Ontario (1999) and continued severe drought in the Prairies. From 1985 to 1999, 380 weather-related natural disasters occurred in Canada and resulted in 240 deaths, $14.3 billion in economic losses and $3.2 billion in insured losses (see Figure 2-1).

Health Effects

Extreme weather events are deadly – according to the World Meteorological Organization, it is estimated that weather- and climate-related disasters claim nearly 225,000 lives a year globally. Any increase in the frequency or intensity of extreme weather events would worsen this serious situation. The severity of extreme weather events depends upon several factors, the most important being the

BOX 2-4

Protect Yourself from Temperature Extremes

- The best defence against heat-related illness is prevention — stay cool inside an air conditioned building, even if it is just for a couple of hours a day. If your home does not have air conditioning, choose other places that you can go to get relief from the heat (e.g., shopping malls, libraries or theatres).

- Increase your water intake even if you don't feel thirsty (avoid alcoholic beverages — they only cause further dehydration).

- If you must be outside, limit your activities and don't plan to do them during the warmest part of the day (between 11 am and 4 pm).

- Wear lightweight, light-coloured clothing. Light colours will reflect away the sun's rays more than dark colours, which absorb the sun's rays.

- Protect your face and head by wearing a wide-brimmed hat. A hat will keep direct sunlight off your head and face.

- Listen to weather reports for "Humidex Advisories" issued by Environment Canada and change your behaviour accordingly (i.e., avoid unnecessary outdoor activities when the humidex is above 40°C). Humidex is a measure of how hot we feel, taking into account the combined effect of temperature and humidity. Advisories are issued when temperatures are expected to exceed 30°C, and when humidex values are expected to exceed 40°C.

BOX 2-5

What's Being Done?

The City of Toronto has already begun to protect vulnerable people during heat waves by utilizing the Toronto Heat/Health Alert system, which was introduced during the summer of 2001. Custom made for Toronto's weather conditions, the system forecasts the occurrence of oppressive heat before it happens. The system is adjusted for the local climate and takes into account how people have responded to certain weather conditions in the past. By using historical meteorological data combined with mortality data, experts were able to conclude which weather conditions resulted in above-average "heat-related" deaths. Two specific air masses were associated with increased deaths: "dry tropical," which is hot and dry conditions, and "moist tropical," which is associated with hot and oppressively humid air. Using this knowledge, the City issues a "heat alert" when the likelihood of weather-related excess deaths occurring exceeds 65 per cent. A "heat emergency" is issued when the likelihood of weather-related excess deaths occurring exceeds 90 per cent.

nature and intensity of the event. For example, because of their violent nature and rate of occurrence, **tornadoes** are the weather events most likely to result in a disaster. Injury and death often result from tornadoes because these storms arise quickly, leaving little time for warning and for seeking safety. **Hurricanes,** on the other hand, have (on average) a lower mortality rate than tornadoes because weather forecasters are able to predict their formation and arrival at a region more accurately, thereby giving people enough time to seek safety and prepare for the storm. Hurricanes, can, however, trigger secondary weather effects, such as landslides and flooding, that, together with high winds, can cause high rates of injury and death.

Figure 2-1

Distribution of Natural Disaster Losses in Canada, 1985–1999 (Munich Reinsurance, 2000)

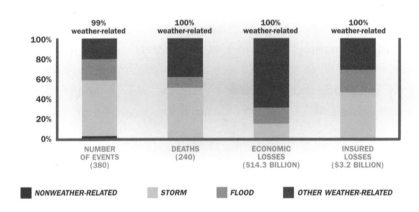

"Storm" includes hurricanes, tornadoes and high winds. "Other" includes weather-related events, such as wildfire, landslides, avalanches, extreme temperature events, droughts, lightning, frost and ice/snow damages.

Source: Climate Change 2001: Working Group II: Impacts, Adaptation and Vulnerability. Contribution of Working Group II to the Third Assessment Report of the Intergovernmental Panel on Climate Change.

Drowning is the number one cause of death during **floods,** followed by electrocution from contact with water and live wires. The degree to which flooding can cause injuries and deaths largely depends on the type of flood. Flash floods from heavy rainfalls in short periods are considered the most deadly because of increased flow and volume of water, as well as a very limited warning period in which to seek safety. Although slow-rising river floods do not have as high a potential for deaths, they often cause injury, usually from slips and falls or from sharp objects hidden in flowing water. When flooding has subsided, damp and wet conditions are ideal for moulds and fungi to grow on interior surfaces, which can lead to respiratory problems for allergic people. Floodwater can also be heavily contaminated with sewage, toxins and other pollutants that pose serious health hazards.

In Canada, **drought** is more associated with crop failure and economic losses than with human health impacts. However, municipal water supplies are often impacted by drought. As water evaporates from community reservoirs or lakes, contaminants can accumulate in higher than usual concentrations. At some point, the water may become unsafe to drink.

Droughts can be interrupted by torrential rains that then lead to an explosion of pest populations (e.g., rodents that can transmit diseases). As well, drought conditions can increase the potential for **forest fires,** which, in turn, can cause loss of life or respiratory distress due to poor air quality, as well as emotional stresses related to mass evacuations. In developing countries, drought has severe health impacts, with widespread crop failure and food shortages resulting in famine.

BOX 2-5 — *continued*

What's Being Done?

The system also involves various outreach activities, including improved access for vulnerable groups to "cooling centres" where bottled water, cots and air-conditioned space are provided. The City has also introduced a "heat information telephone line," promotion of the "buddy system" to call or visit friends, relatives and neighbours who are at increased risk, and increased emergency medical service staffing. Initiatives are also underway to decrease the urban heat island effect through planting shade vegetation and installing cooler surfaces throughout the city.

BOX 2-6

Health Impacts of the Ontario/Quebec Ice Storm (1998)

The deadly ice storm that hit eastern Ontario and southern Quebec in January 1998 is a good example of the adverse health effects that can occur due to extreme weather events. The storm was brought on by a combination of unusual and complex weather conditions that stayed in the region for an extended period of time (January 4–10). The storm resulted in 25 deaths and an estimated 60,000 physical injuries. Much of this can be attributed to a power failure that cut off the electricity supply to 3.6 million persons. Health effects related to the storm included carbon monoxide poisoning, hypothermia, electrocution, food poisoning, flu epidemics, stress and violence, as well as injuries sustained from slips and falls, falling ice, house fires, motor vehicle accidents and chainsaw accidents. While some deaths occurred due to falling branches or power lines, many others resulted from a lack of heat or from misguided attempts to heat homes in unsafe ways.

The displacement of residents into community shelters may have reduced the risk of such accidents, yet it resulted in crowded living conditions conducive to the spread of flu and other infectious diseases. Even after power was restored, there were numerous cases of post-traumatic stress disorder, including anxiety, depression and chronic fatigue.

Rising sea levels and **storm surges** are also of concern as they can cause saltwater to intrude into rivers, lakes and groundwater, thereby reducing the quality and quantity of freshwater supplies. Rising sea levels and storm surges will also lead to flooding of low-level and coastal areas, thereby bringing about related health and safety concerns.

Most large-scale weather disasters result in a significant number of people being crowded into shelters. This can trigger infectious disease outbreaks, especially if water and sewage systems are not operating properly. Evacuation can also bring about psychological disorders, such as stress, anxiety and depression.

The vulnerability of the local population influences the severity of any health impacts. For example, in developed countries where housing and building structures are more able to withstand extreme events, and where early-warning systems are more common, the greatest impacts are usually economic (e.g., loss or damage of property). In contrast, in more vulnerable developing countries, health costs, rather than economic costs, tend to be highest.

Who is at Risk?

Health effects from extreme events can potentially affect all segments of the population and are not necessarily restricted to a certain vulnerable group. However, on the whole, young children, the elderly, those in poor health, or people living in poor quality housing will be most vulnerable to stresses related to weather extremes.

Geography is the dominant risk factor. People living near floodplains or coastal areas will obviously be more at risk from floods and storm surges. Those living in coastal maritime regions are more at risk from hurricanes. According to the federal government, Canada has several high-risk tornado zones, including Alberta, southern Ontario, southern Quebec, and an area that stretches from southern Saskatchewan and Manitoba through to Thunder Bay, Ontario. There are also tornado zones in the interior of British Columbia and in western New Brunswick. In Canada, blizzards are most common in the Prairies and the eastern Arctic. Heavy snowfalls are most common in British Columbia, in some areas around the Great Lakes, in southern and eastern Quebec, and in the Atlantic Provinces. Freezing rain can occur anywhere in the country, but is particularly common from Ontario to Newfoundland.

BOX 2-7

Protect Yourself from Extreme Weather Events

- Make sure your home is safe from the elements. Board up windows during extreme storms.

- Stay indoors and don't travel during extreme weather events.

- Check the weather forecast before embarking on a trip or outdoor activity. Pay special attention to any weather watches, warnings or advisories that may have been issued.

- Find out what roads, areas and buildings are safe. You can usually get this information from public radio or television announcements.

- Do not drive through flooded roads. Cars can be swept away by oncoming water or can break down.

- Be prepared: stock up on heating fuel and ready-to-eat food, as well as battery-powered flashlights and a radio.

Air Pollution

The air we breathe is contaminated with pollutants that negatively impact human health. These pollutants have many sources: natural (e.g., pollen, volcanoes and forest fires), agricultural (e.g., methane, pesticides and herbicides), commercial activities (e.g., dry-cleaning operations and auto body shops), industrial (e.g., fossil fuel-fired electric power plants and manufacturing facilities), transportation (e.g., truck and automobile emissions), and residential (e.g., home gas and oil burners and wood stoves).

Among the pollutants generated from these activities are nitrogen oxides (NO_x), sulphur dioxide (SO_2), and carbon monoxide (CO), as well as a range of organic gases and vapours referred to as volatile organic compounds (VOCs). Ground-level ozone (O_3) is not emitted directly into the air from a specific source, but is created through a photochemical reaction between NO_x and VOCs in the presence of heat and sunlight. Tiny particles, known as "particulate matter" (PM), and that may be either solid or liquid, are also generated

from human activities, particularly fossil fuel combustion. All of these potentially toxic gases and substances are also major contributors to smog, and are together referred to as air pollutants. For more information about smog and what you can do to protect yourself, read Pollution Probe's *Smog Primer* at www.pollutionprobe.org/ Publications/Primers. htm.

Climate change could increase air pollution levels in several ways. First, changes in climate could affect local weather, and thereby local and regional pollution concentrations. Precipitation levels, cloud cover, water vapour levels, and wind speed and direction all affect how pollutants are dispersed and at what concentrations. Some scientists have suggested that the formation of smog will increase with mean annual temperature increases as the smog precursors of NO_x and VOCs react faster at higher temperatures and create more ground- level ozone. As a result, frequent and severe heat waves could translate into more frequent high-ozone-level days and air pollution advisories. The Ontario Medical Association has estimated that the number of premature deaths in Ontario attributable to high smog levels will increase from 1,925 in the year 2000 to 2,573 by 2015.

Secondly, climate change will affect natural sources of air pollutant emissions, such as forest fires. Increased drought brought on by climate change could influence the occurrence of forest fires since they usually need dry conditions to start. When forests and other vegetation burn, particulate matter is released into the air. Also released into the air are large amounts of CO, NO_x, SO_2 and VOCs. If there are no winds to blow the pollutants away, the air can remain hazardous for weeks. If wind is present, the pollutants can be spread over a large region: in early July 2002, the northeastern part of the United States felt the effects of fires burning in northern Quebec, with elevated particulate matter concentrations recorded in many areas of the New England and mid-Atlantic states.

Thirdly, climate change could bring about increases in human-made emissions. With higher temperatures, greater amounts of fossil fuels (e.g., coal) would be burned by power plants to satisfy increased air conditioning demands, thus producing more greenhouse gases and smog-causing pollutants.

Fourthly, climate change will change the distribution and types of airborne allergens, such as pollen. Studies have shown that rising levels of CO_2 will bring about an increase in the production of pollen in some plants, producing more allergens and thereby making the situation worse for those people suffering from asthma, emphysema and other respiratory illnesses.

BOX 2-8

Health Co-benefits

The burning of fossil fuels — the main cause of greenhouse gas emissions and climate change — is also a principal source of air pollution, particularly urban smog. A number of measures that reduce air pollution (such as reducing car use, conserving energy or converting coal-fired power plants to natural gas) will also reduce greenhouse gas emissions. Likewise, most measures to reduce greenhouse gas emissions will also reduce air pollution. These improvements are known as "health co-benefits."

Protect Yourself from Air Pollution

- On smoggy days, avoid outdoor strenuous work or exercise. The faster you breathe the more pollution you take into your lungs.

- Stay indoors as much as you can during days when pollution levels are high.

- If you must be outside, avoid being around high traffic areas or during peak rush hours to minimize your exposure to smog. As well, stay out of the direct sun and drink lots of water.

Changes in precipitation and temperature are also likely to influence the growth and distribution of allergen sources, such as ragweed. An accompanying increase in humidity would also mean a rise in the production of mould spores.

Health Effects

There is already extensive evidence of the health effects that result from air pollution. The damaging effects of exposure to smog can range from eye, nose and throat irritation to decreased lung function (a decrease in the ability to move air in and out of the lungs). Ground-level ozone can also aggravate respiratory and cardiac disease and, in some cases, cause premature death. Studies have shown that, when smog levels rise, there is an increase in the number of visits to doctors by people with breathing problems, as well as increases in daily respiratory admissions to hospitals. Fine airborne particles, such as those found in smog, have damaging health effects because they are able to penetrate deep into the lungs, causing or worsening cardio-respiratory problems.

With a warmer and wetter climate resulting in higher airborne concentrations of various pollens and spores in some regions, people suffering from allergies and respiratory disorders could suffer health impacts. People with asthma have bronchial tubes that can be easily inflamed, therefore particulates, which can irritate and inflame air passages, are likely to greatly affect this group. A number of studies have found a strong association between increases in the concentration of particulate matter and a rise in the number of emergency room visits and hospital admissions for asthma.

Who is at Risk?

We are all exposed to air pollution and thereby affected by it in some way. There are, however, certain groups of people who are more vulnerable than others to the harmful effects of smog:

- **Children** are especially vulnerable to air pollution because of their high metabolic rate, the fact that their lungs are still developing, and because they spend more time being active outdoors than adults. Hotter, more humid weather could pose special health risks for children who already suffer from asthma.

- Many **older people** suffer from chronic respiratory and heart conditions, or from other pulmonary and circulatory stresses, all of which may be worsened by the inhalation of particulate matter and other pollutants. A number of studies have linked particulate matter with increased hospital admissions for cardiovascular and respiratory problems in the elderly, as well as with premature death.

- **People who exercise outdoors,** such as cyclists and runners, expose themselves to higher levels of some pollutants than do people who don't engage in strenuous outdoor exercise. Exercise results in increased heart activity, which in turn requires deep and rapid breathing. When this happens, pollutants are drawn deep into the lungs where they can do considerable damage.

- **People with asthma** and those affected with allergies could be negatively affected by an increase of pollens and airborne allergens in the atmosphere.

Waterborne and Foodborne Contamination

Waterborne diseases are caused by pathogens (disease-causing microorganisms, such as viruses, bacteria and protozoa) spread through contaminated drinking water or recreational water. Foodborne illnesses are caused by food coming in contact with tainted water, or the growth of harmful organisms on food. Climate change could cause an increase in the incidence of water- and foodborne illnesses in a number of ways. Most of the viruses, bacteria and protozoa that cause water- and foodborne diseases thrive in warm water and weather. Therefore, increased water and air temperatures could stimulate the growth of harmful pathogens. In addition, increased rainfall events can lead to these pathogens being deposited in water, thereby leading to contamination. According to a study published in the American Journal of Health, for 68 per cent of all waterborne disease outbreaks in the United States between 1948 and 1994, there was a significant association with preceding heavy rainfall events.

Water can become contaminated by pathogens in several ways, the most common being the improper disposal of sewage and waste. The majority of waterborne microorganisms that cause human disease come from animal and human feces. Sewage, or wastewater, is not supposed to be released raw and untreated into the environment; however, such release may happen inadvertently in communities that use combined sewage and storm water drainage systems, meaning that both storm water and raw sewage are carried through the same pipe to a sewage treatment plant. The increase in volume of water following a heavy rainfall event can overwhelm a treatment plant's capacity. In such cases the overflow is discharged – with limited or no treatment – directly into surface water bodies.

Because the overflow contains untreated human and industrial waste, it can carry potential toxins and pathogens to the receiving waters, thereby contaminating them. Microbial contaminants in freshwater bodies and marine waters have caused eye, ear, nose, skin, respiratory, gastrointestinal and other infections. Studies in Canada and the United States have found increased illness due to swimming in water contaminated by water flow coming through storm drains located near beaches. More significantly, if a water filtration plant's intake is downstream from where the sewage is being discharged, there is a risk of contaminated water getting into the municipal water supply.

Water can also become contaminated through surface runoff during a heavy rainfall, which can allow pathogens to find their way into aquifers, wells and drinking water. Urban land use patterns contribute to this problem. As natural areas are deforested and urbanization creates paved and impermeable surfaces, less water from a heavy rainfall event is absorbed into the soil to replenish groundwater sources (the water supply that naturally runs beneath the surface of the ground) and more of it becomes runoff. As this water passes over agricultural and urbanized land, it can become contaminated with disease-causing pathogens, pesticides and other chemical pollutants. This contaminated runoff will then either be discharged directly into water bodies or pass down through the soil and contaminate groundwater and drinking water wells. A tragic example of this situation occurred in Walkerton, Ontario, in 2000, when accumulated rainfalls that followed a drought period washed bacteria from cattle manure into a shallow town well, thus contaminating the water supply. Seven people died and thousands fell ill after drinking improperly treated water that was polluted with a highly virulent strain of E. coli O157:H7.

BOX 2-10

Protect Yourself from Waterborne and Foodborne Illnesses

- Wash your hands thoroughly and frequently.

- Do not use contaminated water to wash dishes, brush your teeth, wash and prepare food, or make ice.

- Boiling water kills harmful bacteria and parasites. Bringing water to a rolling boil for ten minutes will kill most organisms.

- Do not eat food that may have come into contact with contaminated water.

- When traveling to countries where waterborne or foodborne contamination is prevalent, take precautions. Get vaccinated before you leave and be careful about where and what you eat.

Water can also become contaminated with natural toxins produced by algae. This happens when warm coastal waters combine with nutrient-rich (i.e., fertilizer and sewage) runoff to produce expansive blooms, or "red tides," of toxic algae or "cyanobacteria." These algae can carry potent nerve toxins that are very harmful to humans. Toxic red tides could proliferate as seawater temperatures increase, leading to more fish and shellfish poisonings. Canadian waters have experienced several beach and shellfish bed closings from harmful algal blooms. In 1987, on Prince Edward Island, 107 people were hospitalized and four died as a result of eating contaminated mussels. The outbreak, caused by a naturally occurring algal toxin that attacks the brain, coincided with an El Niño year, when warm currents of the Gulf Stream were near the shore and increased the ocean's water temperature.

Drought can also play a role in water contamination. During a drought period there is less runoff flowing into lakes, ponds and streams. This can lead to low water levels, which means that less water is available to disperse and dilute pollutants. Low water levels also mean higher temperature water and increases in the potential for algae growth.

Food poisoning is associated with warm weather. During warmer weather people more frequently eat outdoors and may leave foods in the sun without proper refrigeration. Higher temperatures favour the multiplication of harmful bacteria, such as Salmonella. For this reason, a seasonal pattern is often observed, with a peak in cases of food poisoning during the summer months (see Figure 2-2).

Individuals may also be exposed to pathogens by eating fresh produce that has been irrigated or cleaned with contaminated water. In 1997, about 150 Michigan students and teachers contracted the foodborne disease hepatitis A after eating imported strawberries. Similar outbreaks have been linked to produce grown outside North America, usually in countries that have inadequate wastewater treatment that can then result in contaminated water used for irrigation.

For information on ways to protect drinking and recreational water sources, see *The Source Water Protection Primer* at www.pollutionprobe.org/ Publications/Primers.htm.

Figure 2-2

Relationship Between Temperature and Monthly Reports of Salmonella Cases in New Zealand (1965–2000)

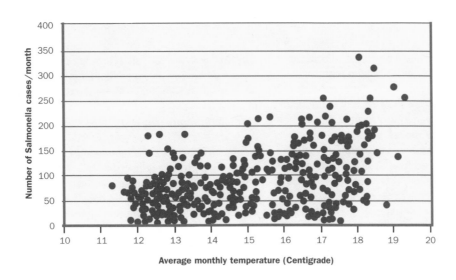

Source: World Health Organization. 2003. *Climate Change and Human Health — Risks and Responses. Summary.*

Health Effects

More than 100 types of pathogenic bacteria, viruses and protozoa can be found in contaminated water, many of which have been implicated in a variety of water- and foodborne illnesses. In Canada, between 1974 and 1996, more than 160 waterborne disease outbreaks, involving some 8,000 people, were reported. It has been estimated that only 10 per cent of all waterborne outbreaks occurring in Canada are reported.

Symptoms of water- and foodborne illnesses include diarrhea, loose or watery stools, stomach cramps and fever. Table 2-1 outlines four of the most common water- and foodborne pathogens in North America that have been linked to climate change.

TABLE 2-1: Health Effects of Common Waterborne/Foodborne Pathogens that have a Weather/Climate Link

PROTOZOA

CRYPTOSPORIDIUM is a microscopic protozoan single-celled parasite that lives in the intestines of animals and people. Cryptosporidium parvum causes a disease called cryptosporidiosis. The parasite is excreted in the feces of infected humans and animals. Infection can occur by drinking water or eating food contaminated with the parasite. Drinking untreated surface water (i.e., from streams, rivers and lakes) or swallowing a small amount of water when swimming, even in a chlorinated pool, can cause cryptosporidiosis. The parasite may also be spread in uncooked foods, beverages and ice prepared with contaminated water. Unwashed fresh fruits and vegetables may carry the parasite if manure was used or animals grazed where the crop was grown. Symptoms include watery diarrhea, abdominal cramps, nausea, low-grade fever, dehydration and weight loss. The tough-walled parasites survive under a wide range of environmental conditions and are not killed by typical household disinfectants, including bleach, but can be killed by boiling

the contaminated water. Cryptosporidium is highly resistant to chlorine and is difficult to remove through filtration because of its microscopic size.

GIARDIA is a microscopic protozoan parasite that is passed along to humans through the ingestion of contaminated water or food. Giardia is often found in human, beaver, muskrat and dog feces. When ingested, the parasites germinate, reproduce and cause illness. The parasites are then passed in the feces. Giardia causes an intestinal illness called giardiasis, more commonly known as "beaver fever." Symptoms include diarrhea, loose or watery stool, stomach cramps and upset stomach. These symptoms may lead to weight loss and dehydration. Some people have no symptoms. Symptoms generally begin one to two weeks after infection. Boiling water will kill Giardia parasites. However, Giardia is highly resistant to chlorine, a commonly used water disinfectant. Due to the small size of the parasite, it is difficult to remove through filtration.

BACTERIA

E-COLI is a type of bacteria commonly found in the intestines of animals and humans. It comes from human and animal wastes. During precipitation, E. coli may be washed into creeks, rivers, streams, lakes and ground water. When drinking water is not treated or is inadequately treated, E. coli may end up in drinking water. E. coli O157:H7 is one of hundreds of strains of the bacterium E. coli. It is the deadly strain that hit Walkerton, Ontario, in 2000. Although most strains are harmless and live in the intestines of healthy humans and animals, this strain produces a powerful toxin that can cause severe illness. Infection often causes severe

bloody diarrhea and abdominal cramps. Frequently, no fever is present. Although most people recover from an E. coli O157:H7 infection, five to 10 per cent of infected individuals go on to develop hemolytic uremic syndrome (HUS) also known as "hamburger disease," a severe life-threatening illness. HUS is the most common cause of kidney failure in childhood. E. coli O157:H7 is responsible for more than 90 per cent of the cases of HUS that develop in North America. In fact, some researchers now believe that E. coli O157:H7 is the only cause of HUS in children. Boiling water will kill the E.coli bacterium.

VIRUSES

THE HEPATITIS A VIRUS (HAV) is found in the feces of people with the liver disease known as hepatitis A. You can get HAV by drinking water or eating food contaminated with the virus. If symptoms are present, they usually occur abruptly and may include fever, tiredness, loss of appetite, nausea, abdominal discomfort, dark urine and jaundice (yellowing of the skin and eyes). Symptoms usually last less than two months; a few persons are ill for as long as six months. The average incubation period for hepatitis A is 28 days. Relapsing hepatitis for up to one year occurs in 15 per cent of cases. Careful hand-washing is one of the best preventive measures against hepatitis A.

Who is at Risk?

For most healthy people, infection from a waterborne pathogen will cause diarrhea for a limited time and will go away without medical treatment. However, in infants, young children, the elderly, pregnant women, and anyone with a weakened immune system, waterborne and foodborne diseases can be very serious and even fatal. Some diseases, such as that caused by the hepatitis A virus, can be serious and long lasting, even in previously healthy people.

Vector-borne and Rodent-borne Infectious Diseases

Insects, such as mosquitoes, ticks and fleas, are called "vectors" when they carry diseases that can be passed on to animals or humans. An insect may contract a disease when it bites an infected animal. If the insect then bites a human, the disease is passed from insect to human. Rodents (e.g., rats, mice and ground squirrels) can also transmit diseases directly to humans through contact with urine, feces, or other body fluids, through skin absorption, and through breathing contaminated air particles.

Different insects can carry different diseases. Diseases associated with mosquitoes include malaria, dengue, yellow fever and viral encephalitis (e.g., West Nile virus). Ticks can transmit Lyme disease, Rocky Mountain spotted fever, human ehrilichiosis, tularemia and Colorado tick fever. Diseases transmitted by fleas include the plague and flea-borne typhus. Rodent-borne diseases include Hantavirus Pulmonary Syndrome (HPS) and Leptospirosis.

For humans to contract vector- or rodent-borne diseases usually requires three conditions: 1) a human and/or animal "host" for the disease; 2) a large enough population of insects or rodents; and, 3) a temperature range that supports this population. Present Canadian climatic conditions allow for the survival of several vector/rodent-borne diseases, including Lyme disease (127 cases reported between 1981 and 1998), West Nile virus fever (851 probable human cases reported in 2003) and Hantavirus Pulmonary Syndrome (32 cases reported since December 1999). Warmer temperatures associated with climate change may enable vectors – and the diseases they carry – to extend their ranges and increase their populations. As temperatures increase, the chance of humans contracting the diseases may therefore also increase.

In less than five years, for example, West Nile virus has spread from an initial isolated outbreak around New York City in 1999 to being found in bird populations across most of North America in 2003. In Canada an increase in the number of human cases has coincided with the spread of the disease westward across the country. In 2002, Ontario had over 90 per cent of the confirmed 340 cases of West Nile virus; while in 2003 the vast majority of cases were recorded in the Prairies

(736 probable cases in Saskatchewan, and 270 confirmed cases in Alberta).

The introduction of diseases not currently within Canada, such as malaria, yellow fever, dengue fever and the plague, is also a concern related to climate change. In tropical countries where these diseases already exist, the number of incidences is expected to increase dramatically.

A changing climate can influence the spread of vector-borne diseases in several ways. Firstly, climate determines the survival rates of bloodsucking insects, particularly mosquitoes, fleas and ticks. For people who live in a cooler climate, it is likely that mosquitoes are not around all year because winter freezing kills many eggs, larvae and adults.

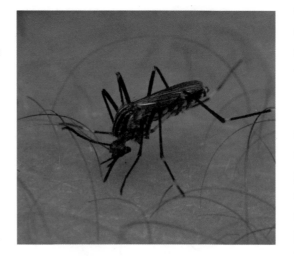

However, if there are fewer freezing episodes over a winter, then more mosquitoes will survive or "over-winter," resulting in a larger population the following spring. While the recent introduction of West Nile virus into the United States and into Ontario cannot be directly related to climate change, the subsequent spread of the virus has been associated with the over-wintering of mosquitoes combined with a series of weather events that took place over the 1998–1999 winter (see Figure 2-3). Studies have suggested that temperature increases the ability of mosquitoes to transmit the West Nile virus by influencing the survival of the pathogens within the insect (i.e., the incubation period – the time from infection of the vector to transmission to humans – decreases with increasing temperatures). For example, one study found that, in 30°C temperatures, greater than 90 per cent of all mosquitoes contained infection after 12 days; at 18°C, less than 30 per cent contained infection after 28 days. Therefore, diseases will reproduce faster inside the vector as the climate warms.

Increases in temperature can also affect vector development and population growth. For example, high temperatures can increase the rate at which mosquito larvae develop into adults. Faster adult development means faster generational turnover, which means more mosquitoes.

Floods – another consequence of climate change – could lead to mosquito population

BOX 2-11

Protect Yourself from Vector/Rodent-borne Diseases

- Spend less time outdoors in the evenings when mosquitoes are more active.

- Equip your house with window and door screens.

- To control mosquito populations, drain all standing water left in containers around your home.

- Wear insect repellents when in areas where mosquitoes are likely to be found (see Box 2-12).

- Wear long sleeves and pants when outdoors in wooded areas where ticks can be found.

- Control mice and rat populations around your work or home.

- When traveling to lesser-developed countries where diseases such as malaria are common, get vaccinated before you leave. While in the affected country, take precautionary measures to reduce your risk of exposure to mosquitoes.

Figure 2-3 **Weather and the Spread of the West Nile Virus in New York City, Summer 1999**

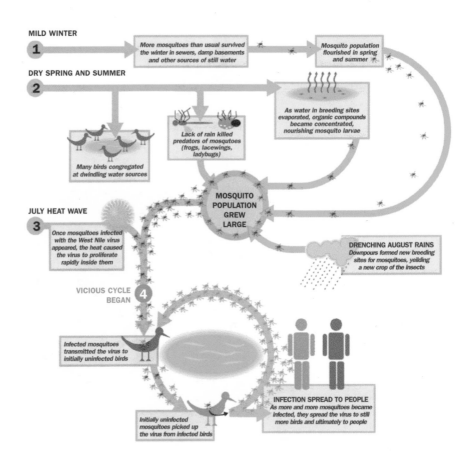

This diagram offers a possible explanation for how a warming trend and sequential weather extremes helped the West Nile virus to become established in the New York City area in 1999.

Source: Epstein, P. 2000.

booms. After floods recede, they leave behind standing water and puddles – perfect breeding grounds for mosquitoes. A growth in the population of mosquitoes would create a greater opportunity for the spread of disease. Longer summers and earlier springs would also extend the mosquito season in Canada.

Rodent-borne pathogens are less directly affected by climate; however, variable and extreme weather conditions can affect rodents' food supply, which in turn can influence their range and population size. For example, an outbreak of Hantavirus Pulmonary Syndrome in the southeastern United States was attributed to the combination of a prolonged drought, which reduced the number of rodent predators, followed by heavy rains, which increased the rodent food supply of grasshoppers and pine nuts. The result was a population explosion of deer mice and other rodents that carry the virus. With the return of drought later in the summer, rodents sought food near human settlements, thereby bringing the disease to people living there.

Introduction of New Diseases

Along with growing concern about the spread of existing diseases, comes the threat of the introduction of new diseases to Canada as a result of warmer temperatures. For a disease to be introduced to a region, the climate must be favourable for survival of both the vector and the pathogen. History has proven that some areas of North America have a favourable climate for certain vectors and pathogens. From the 1600s to the mid-1900s, malaria was widespread throughout much of the United States and Eastern Canada, and outbreaks of dengue and yellow fever occurred regularly during the summer months. In the 1900s, there were epidemics of mosquito-borne diseases, such as St. Louis encephalitis and Western equine encephalitis. Dengue, yellow fever and malaria had disappeared by the middle of the 20th century because of public health measures and better sanitation and housing. In North America, mosquito control measures and changes in lifestyles and living conditions were major factors in the disappearance of these diseases. The question is whether warmer and more hospitable temperatures for vectors and their pathogens could again allow outbreaks of these deadly diseases in North America. The mosquitoes that can carry the malaria pathogens still exist in Canada. There has been sporadic introduction and transmission of malaria in the United States, and Canadian health authorities recorded more than 1,000 cases of malaria per year in the 1990s; however, these were almost entirely due to people infected outside of Canada.

Mosquitoes are sensitive to climate, and are therefore likely to be among the first organisms to extend their range as climate change makes new

BOX 2-12

How Do I Use Mosquito Repellents Safely?

Always follow product instructions. Apply repellent lightly to exposed skin and to clothing. Never use over cuts, wounds, or sunburned or irritated skin. Avoid applying to children's hands, face and eyes. If repellent gets in the eyes, rinse with water right away. When using a spray, avoid breathing it in, and always spray in a well-ventilated area (e.g., do not spray DEET while inside a tent). Don't spray near food. Avoid prolonged use and wash repellent off daily. Health Canada recommends the following:

Children under six months of age
• Do NOT use insect repellents containing DEET.

• Use mosquito netting and avoid the outdoors during dusk and dawn.

Children six months to two years
• Use a product containing 10 per cent DEET or less.

• Maximum of one application per day.

Children two to 12 years of age
• Use a product containing 10 per cent DEET or less.

• Maximum of three applications per day.

areas more accessible. Tropical diseases carried by mosquitoes would extend north as climate change raises global temperatures. According to an Environment Canada report, malaria could return to southern Canada, and dengue and yellow fever may extend northward into Canada. In fact, small outbreaks of diseases carried by mosquitoes are now occurring both north and south of tropical regions. Since 1990, the beginning of the warmest decade in the past 1,000 years, outbreaks of locally transmitted malaria have occurred during heat waves in Texas, Florida, Georgia, Michigan, New Jersey and New York. These episodes were most likely started by infected travelers or mosquitoes coming from a country where malaria is active. However, Canada already has the climate conditions necessary for survival of the malaria parasite. With the increase in international travel and population movement, coupled with the prediction of an additional 50 to 80 million cases of malaria to occur worldwide each year as a result of climate change, the opportunity for pathogens to move globally and flourish in the favourable climate of Canada has been greatly heightened.

Health Effects

The health effects of vector/rodent-borne diseases depend on the pathogen, along with the health status of the infected individuals. Some key vector/rodent-borne diseases that may affect Canadian's health with warmer temperatures are described below.

Lyme Disease: Lyme disease bacteria can be transmitted to humans by the bite of infected deer ticks. Within days to weeks following a tick bite, 80 per cent of patients will have a red, slowly expanding rash, accompanied by general fatigue, fever, headache, stiff neck, muscle aches and joint pain. If untreated, weeks to months later some patients may develop more severe symptoms, including episodes of swelling and pain in the large joints, nervous system abnormalities, motor and sensory nerve inflammation, inflammation of the brain and, rarely, cardiac problems. Lyme disease is seldom, if ever, fatal.

Hantavirus Pulmonary Syndrome (HPS): Some rodents (in Canada, usually deer mice) are infected with types of hantaviruses that cause HPS. These rodents shed the viruses in their urine, droppings and saliva. The viruses are mainly transmitted to people when they breathe in contaminated air. In Canada, deer mice are the only known vector for hantavirus. Early symptoms of HPS include fatigue, fever and muscle aches, especially the large muscle groups. Other symptoms include headaches, dizziness, chills and/or abdominal problems, such as nausea, vomiting, diarrhea and abdominal pain. About half of all HPS patients experience these symptoms.

The mortality rate for HPS is very high in both the United States and Canada, reaching approximately 40 per cent in otherwise healthy individuals. As of December 1999, 32 laboratory-confirmed cases of HPS had been reported in Canada, with 12 of those cases being fatal.

West Nile Virus: West Nile virus is spread by mosquitoes, which can infect people, horses, many types of birds, and other animals when they bite them. Most people who are infected with the West Nile virus will not have any symptoms, or only a mild illness. It is estimated that 20 per cent of the people who become infected will develop West Nile fever. Occasionally a skin rash may develop on the trunk of the body, and there may be swollen lymph glands. Symptoms will generally last a few days.

On rare occasions, West Nile virus infection can result in severe, and sometimes fatal, illnesses. The symptoms of severe infection are West Nile encephalitis (swelling of the brain) or meningitis (inflammation

BOX 2-12 — *continued*

How Do I Use Mosquito Repellents Safely?

Toronto Public Health recommends products containing 10 per cent DEET or less because studies show that lower concentrations of DEET are just as effective, although they don't last as long. Health Canada considers any product containing up to 30 per cent DEET safe for persons 12 years of age and older. Repellent should be re-applied after the protection time listed on the product has elapsed.

Pregnant and breastfeeding mothers
- There is no evidence that the use of DEET by a pregnant woman harms the fetus or affects a nursing child through breast milk. However, non-chemical methods to reduce mosquito bites should be considered.

Source: Toronto Public Health. Summer 2003. *Fact Sheet: West Nile Virus Precautions.*

of the membrane around the brain and spinal cord), which can include headache, high fever, neck stiffness, stupor, disorientation, coma, tremors, convulsions, muscle weakness and paralysis. It is estimated that one in 150 persons infected with the West Nile virus will develop a more severe form of disease. Symptoms of severe disease may last several weeks, although nervous system effects may be permanent.

Leptospirosis: Leptospirosis is spread mainly by the urine of infected rodents, such as rats. Humans and animals can become infected through contact with this contaminated urine. Leptospirosis can cause a wide range of symptoms in humans, though some infected persons may have no symptoms at all. Symptoms of leptospirosis include high fever, severe headache, chills, muscle aches, vomiting, jaundice (yellow skin and eyes), red eyes, abdominal pain, diarrhea and rash. If the disease is not treated, the patient could develop kidney damage, meningitis, liver failure and respiratory distress. In rare cases, death can occur.

Rocky Mountain Spotted Fever: Rocky Mountain spotted fever is a disease caused by infection with *Rickettsia rickettsii* bacteria. This organism is usually carried by two types of ticks: the American dog tick in the eastern and central United States, and the Rocky Mountain wood tick in the Rocky Mountain states and southwestern

Canada. Initial signs and symptoms of the disease include the sudden onset of fever, headache and muscle pain, followed by the development of a rash. The disease can be difficult to diagnose in the early stages, and without proper treatment it can be fatal.

Malaria: Malaria is a life-threatening disease caused by protozoan blood parasites transmitted by mosquitoes. Today, approximately 40 per cent of people living in the world's poorest countries are at risk of getting malaria. Malaria is transmitted to humans through the bite of an infected mosquito. Typically, malaria produces fever, headache, vomiting and other flu-like symptoms. The infection can become life threatening if proper drugs are not available. Malaria can kill by infecting and destroying red blood cells and by clogging the capillaries that carry blood to the brain and other vital organs.

Who is at Risk?

Farmers, grain handlers, hikers, campers and people in occupations that have contact with rodents or mosquitoes or their habitats are at risk. Such occupations include telephone installers, oil workers, plumbers, electricians, pest control officers and certain construction, maintenance and wildlife workers.

People who are active outdoors – anglers, farmers, loggers, trappers, field scientists, campers and hikers – should look for and avoid ticks and mosquitoes.

Travelers to countries where diseases such as yellow fever, dengue fever and malaria are present are also at risk. These diseases are expected to increase worldwide as a result of climate change, thereby increasing the chances of travelers contracting them. It is important to note, however, that the increased risk may be offset by the development of vaccines for some of these diseases (e.g., a vaccine for yellow fever is now available).

Ozone Depletion

The Earth's atmosphere is made up of several distinguishable layers. The layer closest to the surface is called the troposphere. It extends from the Earth's surface to a height of about 10 kilometres. The stratosphere is located in the range of 10 to 50 kilometres above the Earth's surface. The ozone layer is located within the stratosphere. Stratospheric ozone is the Earth's natural protection against damaging ultraviolet radiation; without it, life on Earth could not survive.

Ozone depletion refers to the destruction of stratospheric ozone by certain chemicals, such as CFCs and HCFCs. These human-made gases are used in cooling and other processes. They have accumulated in the atmosphere during the past few decades following their release from air conditioners, refrigerators and aerosol products. These gases all contain chlorine, bromine or fluorine, which destroy ozone.

Ozone depletion and climate change are two different atmospheric problems that concern us; however, they are linked in important ways. The first and most direct link is that some of the gases that are causing ozone depletion, such as CFCs and HCFCs, are also greenhouse gases that are warming the Earth's surface. Secondly, climate change could create favourable conditions in the stratosphere for ozone depletion, particularly over polar regions.

While greenhouse gases have an overall warming effect on the Earth's surface, they have an opposite, cooling effect in the stratosphere. Greenhouse gases act like a blanket, trapping heat near the surface of the Earth, thereby allowing less heat to reach the stratosphere and making it cooler.

Figure 2-4

Regions of the Atmosphere

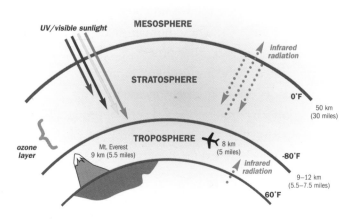

Source: www.noaa.gov.

Moreover, the addition of CO_2 to the stratosphere changes the rate at which energy is radiated out into space. The added CO_2 allows more energy to be radiated out of the stratosphere than comes into it, resulting in cooling. The ozone destruction process over the polar regions is enhanced by the presence of ice clouds (called polar stratospheric clouds) that need very cold conditions to form. This is why the "ozone holes" are found above the polar regions. Ozone destruction happens in mid-latitudes as well; however, the destruction over the poles occurs more rapidly due to several factors, including colder temperatures, the presence of polar stratospheric clouds and the return of sunshine.

Extensive stratospheric ozone losses have occurred over both the Arctic and Antarctic polar regions. Chemistry-climate models suggest that the lowest ozone levels are expected to occur before 2020. Although CFCs have been banned in developed countries, they are still being produced in developing countries and are being released from aging equipment in all countries, including Canada. CFCs are very persistent chemicals, remaining in the atmosphere anywhere from a few decades to a few centuries. The atmospheric concentrations of ozone-depleting chemicals in the stratosphere were near peak levels during the 1990s, and they reached an absolute peak in 2000–2001. The continued cooling of the stratospheric layer will create ideal conditions for continued ozone destruction over the poles. Over the longer term (30–50 years) the size of the ozone holes over the polar areas is expected to decrease as chlorine, fluorine and bromine levels in the atmosphere start to decline due to the controls implemented as a result of the Montreal Protocol (see Box 2-13). However, with less ozone currently protecting the Earth from above, more harmful radiation from the sun is reaching humans living on Earth below. This aspect of climate change can have significant consequences for humans and other animals and organisms. The effects on human health are described below.

43

CHAPTER TWO: **CLIMATE CHANGE AND HUMAN HEALTH**

Health Effects

The sun radiates energy through the atmosphere in the form of invisible ultraviolet (UV) rays. In small doses, UV radiation initiates the production of Vitamin D to build and maintain bones. UV radiation is also absorbed by the DNA in plants and animals. In larger doses, UV absorption can damage DNA and lead to serious human health problems, such as skin and eye damage, as well as skin cancer.

UV radiation is emitted in different wavelengths that vary in their ability to penetrate the ozone layer and reach the surface of the Earth (see Figure 2-5). UVB and UVA rays are largely responsible for skin cancer. Usually, only a small percentage of the sun's UVB reaches the Earth's surface because it is absorbed in the stratospheric ozone layer. However, less stratospheric ozone means less protection and hence more damaging UVB light that reaches the Earth's surface.

Figure 2-5

UV Wavelength

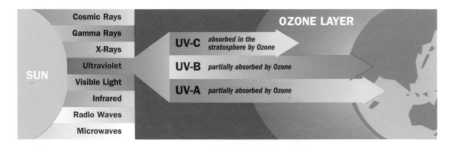

Generally, the shorter the wavelength, the more biologically damaging UV radiation can be if it reaches the Earth in sufficient quantities. UVC wavelengths are the shortest and are mostly blocked by ozone in the stratosphere. UVB and UVA are only partially blocked by ozone. A decrease in ozone will allow more of these wavelengths to reach the Earth's surface.

Source: National Oceanic and Atmospheric Administration (NOAA).

BOX 2-13

The Montreal Protocol (1987)

The production of CFCs and HCFCs is being eliminated under an international agreement titled The Montreal Protocol on Substances that Deplete the Ozone Layer (1987). However, HFC levels are expected to increase rapidly as they replace CFCs for use in refrigeration and air conditioning units. Because HFCs do not contain chlorine, they do not damage the ozone layer; however, they are still powerful greenhouse gases.

The ozone layer over Canada has thinned by about four per cent since the early 1980s. Research has indicated that in areas of lower than normal stratospheric ozone, UVB intensity increases, which could lead to a four per cent increase in basal carcinomas (the most common type of skin cancer) and a six per cent increase in squamous-cell carcinomas (the second most common type of skin cancer). These cancers are relatively easy to treat, if detected in time, and are rarely fatal. However, exposure to UVB and UVA has also been linked to malignant melanoma – a much more serious and deadly type of cancer. It has been estimated that, in 2003, melanoma killed 840 Canadians. Most skin cancers occur on parts of the body that are repeatedly exposed to the sun (e.g., the head, shoulders, back, chest, arms and lower legs).

UV radiation can also cause eye damage, particularly to the cornea, which is a good absorber of UV light. High doses of UV light (e.g., light reflected off snow or ice) can cause a temporary clouding of the cornea, called "snow-blindness." In most cases, snow blindness disappears when a person rests his/her eyes and remains indoors. However, continual and long-term exposure has been linked to the formation of cataracts, which cause permanent blurred or fuzzy vision and blindness.

Overexposure to UV radiation can also impair the body's ability to fight diseases. When skin has been overexposed to UV radiation, the activity of disease-fighting white blood cells within the body is suppressed, thereby affecting the immune system. As a result, the body fails to produce enough of the antibodies required for defence against a variety of diseases.

Who is at Risk?

Several factors make certain groups of people more prone to UV-related health effects. They include people who:

- have red or blonde hair, are fair-skinned or have light-coloured eyes;

- sunburn easily;

- have many moles, freckles or birthmarks;

- work or play outside;

- have had extensive sun exposure as a child or a serious sunburn in early adulthood;

- have experienced strong intermittent recreational sun exposure (particularly indoor workers with unacclimatized skin);

- have family members who have had skin cancer;

- live at high altitudes where sunshine and UV radiation are more intense; and,

- frequently get a tan in the sun or with a sunlamp.

BOX 2-14

Protect Yourself — Environment Canada's UV Index

The UV Index forecast is included in the weather forecast when greater than two. It is a forecast of the maximum intensity of the UVB rays at solar noon. The higher the number, the stronger the intensity of the UVB rays and the greater the need to take precautions.

UV INDEX	CATEGORY	SUN PROTECTION ACTIONS
0 – 2	LOW	Minimal protection for normal activity.
3 – 5	MODERATE	Cover up. Wear hat, sunglasses, sunscreen if outside for 30 minutes.
6 – 7	HIGH	Protection required. Reduce time in sun between 11 am and 4 pm.
8 – 10	VERY HIGH	Take full precautions and avoid sun between 11 am and 4 pm.
11 +	EXTREME	Take full precautions and avoid sun between 11 am and 4 pm.

When the UV Index is eight or more, UVB is extremely strong, and light, untanned skin can burn in 15 minutes or less. Even if you do not get a burn, you may still be damaging your skin.

chapter 3

The Geography of Climate Change Across Canada

G lobal climate models indicate that future changes in temperature will be greatest at high latitudes. Therefore, the magnitude of climate change in a northern country, such as Canada, will be greater than in southern countries. However, not all regions across the country will be equally affected. For example, it is projected that by 2050, temperatures could increase 4–6°C in central and Northern Canada, while the eastern and western coastlines could experience a 3–4°C increase. In part, this is because of the spatial diversity in Canada's climate (e.g., arctic climates of the north versus temperate climates of the south) as well as the enormous diversity in physical landscapes (e.g., mountainous regions in the west, flat central prairie landscapes and eastern coastal regions).

While some of the health impacts of climate change may be seen across all regions of Canada, other impacts could be unique to a specific region or province (e.g., risks associated with sea level rise in the Maritimes). This chapter focuses on some of the more significant impacts on ecosystems and human health that various regions can expect to experience this century as the concentration of greenhouse gases in the atmosphere doubles (and possibly triples). In turn, many of these impacts will have direct and indirect implications for human health.

British Columbia

In British Columbia, average annual temperatures have warmed during the 20th century by 0.6°C on the coast, 1.1°C in the interior, and 1.7°C in the north (see Figure 3-1). Average spring and night time temperatures, in particular, are warmer now than they were 100 years ago. Precipitation has increased by about two to four per cent each decade in southern British Columbia. By the end of the 21st century, average temperatures in British Columbia will likely be 1–4°C warmer than they are now, depending on the region. There are a number of potential consequences:

Sea Level Rise and Flooding: With the exception of the outer coast of Vancouver Island, sea levels rose by four to 12 centimetres along most of the BC coast during the 20th century.

Figure 3-1

Change in Average Temperature in British Columbia, 1895–1995

(°C per century)

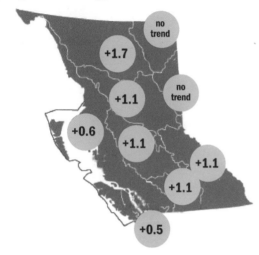

Source: Government of British Columbia. 2002. *Indicators of Climate Change for British Columbia.*

Higher sea levels increase the risk of flooding along the flat, low-lying deltas that make up much of the southern BC coast. This, in turn, could create drainage problems and overwhelm municipal sewage systems in some coastal communities, resulting in water contamination. Saltwater could also intrude into the groundwater, making it unfit to drink. Over the next 100 years the sea level could rise as much as 88 centimetres along parts of the BC coast. The effect will be greater in areas such as the Fraser River delta where 100 square kilometres of land are at an elevation within one metre of sea level, and in Prince Rupert where extreme high water events occur three times more frequently than in other areas of the coast. The steep and rocky areas of the BC coast will likely be less sensitive to sea level rise.

Air Pollution: With the average temperature of BC projected to increase by 1–4°C, smoggy days would also likely increase. Vancouver, Penticton, Kelowna and some other cities in southern British Columbia lie within valleys whose mountain walls trap polluted air. Airborne pollutants are usually dispersed by winds, but on calm days they can become concentrated beneath layers of warmer air. As a result, heat-related and respiratory illnesses may increase.

Landslides: Average precipitation increased over most of southern BC during the 20th century. A wetter climate, combined with increased glacial melt in mountainous regions, would mean less stable slopes and more landslides. Of particular concern are "debris flows" – watery surges of mud, gravel and boulders that travel at high speeds down mountain streams during heavy rains. These flows can strike with little or no warning. A debris flow swept through a community near Kelowna, BC, in 1990, killing three people and causing great damage.

Forest Fires: In summer, warmer temperatures may promote increased evaporation and loss of soil moisture, particularly in the interior regions of BC. These drier conditions may lead to more forest fires, such as those that occurred in the summer of 2003 (see Figure 3-2). Forest disease and pest infestations, such as those caused by the Mountain Pine Beetle, may also increase as warmer summers place additional stress on trees and warmer winters increase pest survival.

Reduced Glacial Flow: In southern BC, the Helm and Illecillewaet Glaciers both receded by more than one kilometre from 1895 to 1995. In the short term, retreating glaciers may add water to mountain-fed streams and rivers. In the long term, significant retreat of large glaciers would mean less runoff, particularly in the summer months (i.e., lower summer flows occur because snow and ice sources have already melted by that time, and because higher summer temperatures increase evaporation). Lower flows lead to warmer water temperatures and declining water quality.

Figure 3-2

BC Forest Fires

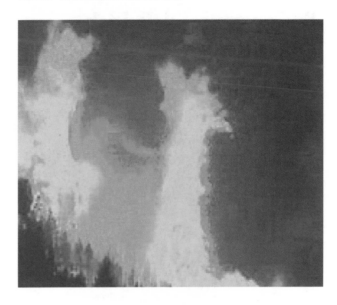

2003 was the worst year for BC forest fires, with nearly 2,500 forest fires burning 2,650 square kilometres of land, bush and residential areas — 11 times the annual average area burned over the past 10 years.

Source: Environment Canada.

The Prairies
(Alberta, Saskatchewan and Manitoba)

The yearly average temperature in the Prairie provinces has warmed by about 1.2°C over the past 50 years; winter temperatures have warmed by about 3°C and summer temperatures have warmed by about 0.2°C. Since 1948, seven of the top ten warmest years on the Prairies occurred after 1981. Due, in part, to their location in the middle of a continent and at relatively high latitudes, Saskatchewan and Manitoba are likely to face earlier and more severe climate change than other parts of Canada (i.e., summer temperatures warming by 3–5°C and winter temperatures by 5–8°C by 2080). As a result, the region will likely experience warmer and wetter winters and springs, and longer, warmer and drier summers. These changes would bring about the following consequences:

Drought: Drought is the most significant climatic characteristic of the Prairies, particularly in the south. Parts of the Prairies experienced severe drought in 2001, which carried over into 2002 and is still currently a high risk. Soil moisture is depleted over much of the western Prairies, and winter snowfall has remained well below normal. Summer precipitation in the Prairies is projected to decline 10–20 per cent and evaporation is expected to increase. As a result, droughts may become even more severe in the future. Some scientists believe that, in the next 30 years, conditions may become as severe as the 10-year "Dust Bowl" drought of the 1930s. With drought comes the increased threat of forest fires, dust storms and related health risks.

Extreme Temperatures and Weather: The Canadian Prairies have seasonal temperature differences greater than in any other part of Canada, with temperatures varying from about -40°C to +40°C. In fact, the hottest temperature recorded to date in Canada was 45°C on July 5, 1937 in southeastern Saskatchewan. The Prairies also regularly experience other severe weather conditions, such as extremely heavy rainfalls and storms ranging from winter blizzards to summer tornados. These extreme events, particularly those in the summer, could become more prevalent on the Prairies as the climate warms. In July 2000, the village of Vanguard, Saskatchewan, experienced the largest rainfall event recorded on the Canadian Prairies. The resulting flood caused a number of problems, including contaminating the community water supply.

Reduced Waterflows: With annual evaporation exceeding precipitation on the Prairies, water supply is dependent on glacial and snowmelt runoff from the prairie and mountain regions to replenish lakes, reservoirs, wetlands and groundwater. Climate change could result in the significant retreat of large glaciers, such as the Athabasca Glacier in Alberta. During the past century, drastic reductions in the surface areas of glaciers have resulted in reduced downstream water flows. Glacial melt waters are necessary to maintain water levels; in fact, 87 per cent of the flow at the mouth of the Saskatchewan River is meltwater from the glaciers of the Rocky Mountains. Recent evidence indicates that the amount of glacial water flowing into the Prairie's largest river, the Saskatchewan, has already begun to decrease. Less water from precipitation and glacial runoff could have an enormous impact on water quality across the Prairies. Less water in lakes, ponds and rivers means there would be less dilution of pollutants, such as pesticides, fertilizers and runoff from livestock. People would be at greater risk of contracting waterborne illnesses. Increased nutrient levels could also cause algal blooms, making the water potentially toxic.

Ontario

Across much of Ontario, mean annual temperatures have warmed by 0.5°C–0.6°C over the past 100 years. Scientists estimate that Ontario could warm by an average of 2–5°C in the next 75 to 100 years. Increases would probably be greater in the winter than in the summer. In Southern Ontario, the climate is highly modified by the influence of the Great Lakes, and it is uncertain what influence the lakes will have on these projected temperature changes. There are a number of key impacts:

Heat Waves: Global climate models suggest that over the next 50 years heat waves will increase in frequency, intensity and duration in southern Ontario. Currently, the average number of hot days (over 30°C) in London, Ontario is approximately 15 per year. This is projected to double by 2050 and surpass 50 days by the 2080s. This situation would be worsened by conventional urban growth, which intensifies the heat island effect. An increase in hot days would increase the risk of heat-stress-related health problems, especially among the very old, the very young, and those with chronic lung diseases, such as asthma. According to the report *Towards an Adaptation Action Plan: Climate Change and Health in the Toronto-Niagara Region,* it is estimated that by the mid-2020s the number of heat-related premature deaths among the elderly in the

Toronto/Niagara region could reach 171 to 447 annually during an average summer.

Air Pollution: The highest occurrence of smog in Canada is in the Windsor to Quebec corridor. Hotter days will permit the formation of more ground-level ozone – the main component in smog – thereby exacerbating the already serious smog problem in the region. A greater number of oppressive air masses, which have been linked to increased deaths, are expected to occur in Ontario's smog regions. Significant increases in the concentration of ground-level ozone are also anticipated. Recent health studies have suggested that there is no safe level of human exposure to ground-level ozone and particulate matter, and negative health outcomes are associated with very low levels of exposure, even for healthy individuals. The Ontario Medical Association estimates that more than 2,060 people in Ontario die prematurely each year from the effects of air pollution.

Water Quality in Lakes: Water levels in the Great Lakes have been dropping for the past six years and evaporation has increased significantly. Some global climate models project that, by 2050, higher air temperatures and increased evaporation will take lake levels much lower than they are now, perhaps by more than one metre. The quality of lake water resources could suffer, especially in shallow bodies of water where pollutants would become more concentrated. Higher lake water temperatures would also create a more favourable environment for microbial and algal blooms, further reducing water quality. This would affect municipalities that draw water from nearby lakes. For example, water intakes located in relatively shallow water, such as in Lake St. Clair, may experience increased episodes of supply, odour and taste problems due to insufficient water depth and increased weed growth and algae concentrations.

Vector-borne Diseases: Warmer temperatures could increase the range of some parasites, such as insects and ticks, bringing new infectious diseases to Ontario. A warmer climate and longer frost-free seasons may further encourage the spread of diseases, such as West Nile virus fever, that are already a problem in Ontario. Of the total 466 confirmed human cases of West Nile virus fever reported in Canada in 2003, 89 were Ontario residents.

Quebec

Climate models show a general warming trend within the next century of 1–4°C throughout southern Quebec and 2–6°C in the northern part of the province. The warming would be greater during the winter and more widespread and intense in northern Quebec. Southern Quebec should also receive slightly above seasonal average amounts of precipitation. More northerly regions would receive 10–20 per cent more precipitation than at present. Some key impacts of these changes include the following:

Extreme Weather Events: Extreme weather events are not new in Quebec. Floods, which occur most frequently in the southern part of the province, are the most common type of natural disaster in Quebec. In summer, the regions of Montreal and Montérégie are most affected by extreme weather, with more than 20 events – violent winds, torrential rains and flooding, and hail – reported in these areas each year. Two of the worst extreme weather, disasters in Canada's history occurred in Quebec. In January 1998, an ice storm left almost half the population of the province without power. In July 1996, intense rainfall caused the Saguenay River to flood, resulting in 10 deaths. Studies suggest that these events could become more frequent in Quebec as the climate changes.

Air Pollution/Heat: Temperatures are likely to be higher in the major centres, such as Montreal, with heat leading to poorer air quality and increased urban smog. Respiratory disorders and allergy problems may worsen, as temperature and humidity rise. More frequent and severe heat waves could lead to more deaths and heat-related health problems, especially in the very young and the elderly.

Figure 3-3

Air Pollution

Poor air quality episodes, such as this one in Montreal, are likely to increase in the coming years.

Source: www.climatechange.gc.ca.

Water Quality: As with the Great Lakes, water levels in the St. Lawrence River could be significantly altered by climate change. Studies suggest that if CO_2 levels in the atmosphere double, as is projected within the next century, the river's annual flow rate could decrease by as much as 40 per cent in Montreal and 30 per cent in Quebec. The St. Lawrence River is a source of drinking water for 45 per cent of Quebecers. This decrease, and subsequent water quality issues, would severely impact a large proportion of Quebec's population.

Atlantic Canada

Atlantic Canada has not followed the national warming trend of the past 100 years. However, with the exception of the coast of Newfoundland, which may experience cooling, the temperatures in Atlantic Canada are projected to increase by 3–4°C over the next 100 years.

Rising Sea Levels: In Atlantic Canada (except Labrador), the sea level has been rising for thousands of years, mainly because the Earth's crust in this area is sinking. At Halifax, Nova Scotia, for example, the sea level has risen about 30 centimetres over the last century. With a projected sea level increase of 70 centimetres on the coast of Nova Scotia by 2100, this could mean the Halifax area will experience an increase of 100 centimetres by the end of this century. According to a report completed by the Geological Survey of Canada, approximately 80 per cent of the Atlantic region's coastline is considered moderately to highly sensitive to global sea level rise.

Storm Surges and Flooding: The Atlantic coast is subjected to frequent heavy storms and the occasional hurricane (e.g., Hurricane Juan in October 2003). A higher sea level combined with large storms may result in more storm surges. Subsequent saltwater intrusion would lead to contamination of groundwater supplies and rivers. Studies have suggested that flooding levels in the Charlottetown region that now occur once every hundred years could occur once every decade before the end of this century. Flooding is already a problem in Newfoundland and Labrador, where flood damages over the past 15 years have exceeded $40 million.

Algal Blooms: Scientists project that a warmer climate will change surface waters and ocean temperatures, thereby creating more favourable conditions for the growth of the organisms responsible for toxic algal blooms, such as red tides. Toxic blooms pose a serious threat to both fish populations and human health.

Figure 3-4

Destruction from Hurricane Juan

Source: Neena Nanda.

The Arctic and Far North

In the past 100 years, the Western Arctic (Mackenzie District) has warmed by 1.5°C, with most of this occurring in winter and spring. The Arctic tundra area (mainland and lowland parts of the Arctic Islands) has warmed by 0.5°C, while the Arctic mountains and fjords of the eastern Arctic have cooled slightly. By the end of the 21st century, winter temperatures over the mainland and much of Arctic Islands could be at least 5–7°C warmer than they are today. Summer temperatures are expected to increase by up to 5°C on the mainland and 1–2°C over marine areas. Annual precipitation is expected to increase up to 25 per cent. There are a number of key impacts of this increase:

Figure 3-5

Average Annual Arctic Ocean Sea Ice Cover

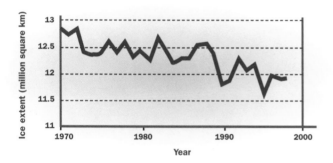

Source: Environment Canada. 2002. *Science and Impacts of Climate Change.*

Changes in Traditional Lifestyles/Food Sources: For indigenous people, the role of subsistence lifestyles (i.e., hunting, trapping, fishing) in maintaining a sense of health and well-being is very important. Subsistence living depends upon both the availability and distribution of wildlife and related resources. Wildlife is sensitive to climate change, with possible consequent changes in their location, habitat and species composition. For example, mainland caribou could lose weight because of heavier snow cover limiting access to their food supply of lichen and moss. In addition, warmer summers could bring about more insect harassment for caribou. This can also cause declines in body fat because caribou would forage less and expend more energy when harassed by mosquitoes and parasitic flies. High Arctic Peary caribou and muskoxen may become extinct, as could polar bears should the Arctic Ocean sea ice continue to shrink (see Figure 3-5). As well, the sea ice is getting thinner, making travel dangerous for hunters. As a result, subsistence patterns (locations, timing, type of game) could change, thereby disrupting the traditional lifestyles of indigenous peoples.

Forest Fires: Drier conditions and more lightning storms are expected to result in an increase in forest fires in the boreal forests of the Northwest Territories and Yukon. In central Yukon, the number of forest fires and the number of hectares burned has been increasing since the 1960s. This trend is expected to continue into the future, as temperatures warm and lightning storms become more frequent.

chapter 4

What is Being Done to Reduce Greenhouse Gases?

C limate change is a global issue affecting the entire planet. Much of the policy response on climate change is being driven by sound science, especially through the Intergovernmental Panel on Climate Change. To date, the focus of the policy response has been on measures to reduce emissions of greenhouse gases. Less attention has been focused on understanding the impacts of climate change and the development of appropriate actions to help Canadians adapt.

Reversing the build-up of greenhouse gases in the Earth's atmosphere over two centuries of fossil fuel powered industrialization will not be easy. Although some negative health effects from climate change may be unavoidable, the extent and severity of health effects can be reduced if progressive action is taken by governments, industry and individuals. Some efforts are being made, both internationally and across Canada, to help prevent what could become an environmental catastrophe. Much more needs to be done.

Actions Taken Internationally

Worldwide, the most significant initiative to take place to date has been the United Nations Framework Convention on Climate Change, ratified by Canada in 1992. The ultimate objective of the convention is to:

"stabilize greenhouse gas concentrations at levels that would prevent dangerous anthropogenic interference with the climate system. Such a level would be achieved within a time-frame to allow ecosystems to adapt naturally to climate change, to ensure that food production is not threatened, and to enable economic development to proceed in a sustainable manner." (UNITED NATIONS FRAMEWORK CONVENTION ON CLIMATE CHANGE, ARTICLE 2 OBJECTIVE).

As part of the Convention, the Kyoto Protocol, an international treaty to reduce greenhouse gas emissions, was adopted in 1997 in Kyoto, Japan. Both reduction and adaptation actions are included in the Convention and the Kyoto Protocol, although the majority of actions to date have focused on greenhouse gas reductions.

The Kyoto Protocol requires industrialized nations to collectively reduce emissions of six greenhouse gases (carbon dioxide, methane, nitrous oxide, HFCs, PFCs and sulphur hexafluoride) by 5.2 per cent below 1990 levels during the period 2008–2012 (referred to as the "Kyoto Commitment Period"). Individual countries' Kyoto targets vary. The European Union, Switzerland and the majority of Central and Eastern European nations must deliver reductions of eight per cent. The United Kingdom has committed to achieving a 12.5 per cent reduction, and has also set its own domestic goal of a 20 per cent reduction in CO_2 emissions by 2010. The United States would have to cut emissions by seven per cent; and Japan, Hungary, Canada and Poland by six per cent. New Zealand, Russia and the Ukraine would be required to stabilize their emissions (i.e., to maintain their greenhouse gas emissions at 1990 levels), while Australia, Iceland and Norway are permitted to increase slightly, although at a reduced rate compared to current trends. These goals for developed countries have to be accomplished during the target period of 2008–2012. Developing countries, including India and China, do not have to commit to reductions in the first commitment period because per person their emissions are much lower than those of developed nations. As well, their economies are less able to absorb the costs related to reducing energy use.

The Kyoto Protocol was endorsed by 160 countries. However, for it to become legally binding, at least 55 countries – representing 55 per cent of the developed world's 1990 emissions – must sign on, or "ratify" it. The European Union ratified in May 2002 and Japan followed suit a month later. Canada was the 100th country to ratify the agreement (in December 2002). Russia was expected to ratify the Kyoto Protocol in 2003, but did not do so. When (and if) Russia ratifies, the Protocol will come into force as a legally binding international protocol. Participating countries around the world would then have to meet their targets for emission reductions. Other countries would be expected to come on board in subsequent negotiations.

Actions Taken by Canada's Federal Government

The federal government monitors and reports on greenhouse gas emissions in Canada. It is also responsible for negotiating Canada's commitments under the Kyoto Protocol (i.e., the reduction of greenhouse gas emissions by six per cent below 1990 levels during the period 2008–2012). The Government of Canada's Climate Change Plan, released in November 2002, includes initiatives designed to reduce Canada's greenhouse gas emissions by 240 megatonnes by 2012. This represents nearly one-third of Canada's Kyoto target. In 2003, the federal government announced the investment of $1 billion from its 2003 budget to go towards the implementation of the plan. This investment builds on $1.7 billion the federal government has invested in climate change since 1998. Measures in the *Climate Change Plan* include:

Transportation

The Government of Canada will

- work with auto manufacturers to improve new vehicle fuel efficiency by 25 per cent by the year 2010, and to increase consumer demand for more efficient vehicles;

- make new investments in programs that will help Canadians make environmentally friendly transportation choices and purchasing decisions;

- increase the amount of gasoline containing 10 per cent ethanol blend (ethanol produces fewer greenhouse gas emissions than regular gas); and,

- encourage the commercial transportation sector to make greater use of alternative fuels and energy-efficient technologies.

Residential and commercial/ institutional buildings:

The Government of Canada will

- create incentives to encourage Canadians to make their homes more energy efficient;

- increase the number of cost-shared home energy audits for homeowners;

- give consumers information about how to purchase energy efficienct appliances and equipment; and,

- work towards having all new homes built to the R-2000 standard of energy efficiency by 2010.

Large industrial emitters:

The Government of Canada will

- establish targets for the industries that produce the most greenhouse gas emissions to reduce their emissions; and,

- share with business the cost of investments that can help reduce emissions, such as renewable energy and clean coal demonstration projects.

Small- and medium-sized enterprises:

The Government of Canada will

- provide information and assistance on the best energy-efficient technologies available to small manufacturers; and,

- promote practices that will reduce emissions.

Actions Taken by Canada's Provincial and Territorial Governments

Provincial and territorial governments have at least partial authority over most of Canada's greenhouse gas emissions. For example, provincial and territorial governments regulate electric utilities, industrial facilities, public transit, building codes, agricultural practices and solid waste management. It is therefore essential that the provinces and territories become fully involved in the national effort to address climate change. Most provinces and territories have developed climate change action plans. These action plans can be found on the province's or territory's government Web site. Some initiatives across Canada include the following:

• The **Province of British Columbia** has taken actions to reduce emissions from its own operations by 16 per cent between 2000 and 2005 by fitting nine facilities in BC Parks with renewable energy sources, such as solar panels and micro-hydro. The government has also purchased 60 hybrid vehicles to encourage the use of this technology. Improvement to the operating efficiency of provincially funded buildings has already resulted in a 45 per cent reduction in energy use. To read more about what the BC government is doing within its own operations to reduce greenhouse gas emissions, go to http://wlapwww.gov.bc.ca/air/climate/#2.

• In 2002, the **Province of Alberta** released an action plan that proposed a provincial approach to addressing the issue of climate change and reducing greenhouse gas emissions. The plan focuses on improving energy efficiency, enhancing the use of technology to control industrial emissions, and seeking out new environmentally friendly sources of energy. For more information about Alberta's actions on climate change, read Albertans and Climate Change: Taking Action, which can be found at www3.gov.ab.ca/env/climate/actionplan.

• The **Province of Saskatchewan** has established a climate change program that is undertaking projects in five major areas: development of public education initiatives; development of new technology to dispose of CO_2; development of strategies to assist in adapting to potential climate change; development of biological sinks for CO_2

in agricultural soils and forests; and implementation of energy conservation and alternative projects. A report entitled *Making it Work: A Saskatchewan Perspective on Climate Change Policy,* which outlines the province's goals and objectives in more detail, can be found at www.ir.gov.sk.ca.

- In 2002, the **Province of Manitoba** announced its intention to meet and exceed Kyoto Protocol reduction targets as part of a national greenhouse gas reduction strategy (i.e., by 2010 Manitoba plans to reduce its emissions up to 18 per cent from 1990 levels as opposed to the six per cent goal to which the whole country has committed). The province expects to meet this goal through the use of renewable energy sources, by capturing emissions from landfill sites, carbon storage and diversified and alternative agricultural practices. For example, the Wuskwatim Hydro Generation Project managed by Manitoba Hydro in partnership with the Nisichawayasihk Cree Nation, is expected to cut greenhouse gas emissions by 1.1 megatonnes per year. The government also announced its intention to require the blending of 10 per cent ethanol in all gasoline sold in the province, thereby potentially reducing emissions by over 0.135 megatonnes per year. Manitoba Hydro has also switched the source of fuel at its Selkirk generating station from coal to natural gas. This initiative alone is expected to cut emissions by

Figure 4-1

Selkirk Generating Station

Source: www.hydro.mb.ca.

0.2 megatonnes per year. To find out more about what the province is doing to combat climate change, read *Kyoto and Beyond: A Plan of Action to Meet and Exceed Manitoba's Kyoto Targets,* found at www.gov.mb.ca/est/climate change.

- In 2002 the **Province of Ontario** announced plans to reduce electricity consumed in its own operations by 10 per cent and a commitment to the goal of ensuring that every newly constructed government and other institutional building will be energy self-sufficient using alternative or clean sources of energy. The Ministry of Energy will also launch a public education campaign that shows consumers how to reduce their consumption and, thus, their electricity bills. Legislation will be introduced making new investments in energy-efficient equipment eligible for a 100 per cent write-off and allowing individuals to claim a tax credit for the cost of solar panels (the goal is to convert 100,000 homes to solar power by 2007). For more information about Ontario's actions on climate change, read *Air Quality and Climate Change: Moving Forward,* found at www.ene.gov.on.ca/envision/air/airclimate/airclimate.htm.

• **The Province of Quebec** is making major investments in public transit in Montreal and Quebec City, as well as creating subsidies for the creation of programs under which employers implement measures to reduce car use by their employees. The government has also developed a plan for reducing greenhouse gas emissions from public buildings by 20 per cent by 2008 (using 1990 as a baseline) while increasing energy efficiency of the entire government vehicle fleet by 20 per cent. For more information about what Quebec is doing, read *Quebec Action Plan on Climate Change 2000–2002* at www.menv. gouv. qc.ca/ changements/plan_action/index-en.htm.

• In August 2001, the premiers and governors of the five eastern Canadian provinces **(New Brunswick, Nova Scotia, Newfoundland and Labrador, Prince Edward Island and Quebec)** and six New England states adopted a Climate Change Action Plan that targets the reduction of regional emissions to 1990 levels by 2010, and to 10 per cent below 1990 levels by 2020. Along with reducing greenhouse gas emissions, the action plan is intended as a foundation for a longer-term shift to cleaner and more efficient ways of using energy, as well as identifying and adopting adaptive measures. New England Governors/Eastern Canadian Premiers Climate Change Action Plan 2001 outlines these initiatives in more detail and can be found at www.negc.org/premiers.html. New Brunswick (www.gnb.ca), Newfoundland and Labrador (www.gov.nf.ca), Nova Scotia (www.gov.ns.ca) and Prince Edward Island (www.gov.pe.ca) are all developing discussion papers, strategies or action plans on climate change that can be viewed on the individual governments' websites.

• In 2001 the **Government of the Northwest Territories** coordinated the development of the Northwest Territories Greenhouse Gas Strategy in partnership with more than 40 federal and territorial agencies, Aboriginal organizations, industry and environment groups. According to the strategy, the objectives are to increase awareness in the Northwest Territories of the issue of global climate change and the need to control greenhouse gas emissions; to engage all northerners including government, non-government, industry and the general public in taking action to control greenhouse gas emissions; to identify and implement achievable and practical actions that can be undertaken immediately, as well as longer-term actions; and to identify economic opportunities that may arise from the use of cleaner, more efficient equipment and technology. For more details read *Northwest Territories Greenhouse Gas Strategy* at www.gov.nt.ca/RWED/eps/climate.htm.

• The **Yukon Government** is working towards a climate change action plan. *An Inventory of Yukon Climate Change Initiatives* was prepared in 2001 as a step towards an action plan; it can be accessed at www.environmentyukon.gov.yk.ca/epa/content/initiatives.pdf.

Actions Taken by Canada's Municipal Governments

There are more than 4,000 municipal governments in Canada. They have a key role to play because they regulate many issues and activities that contribute to climate change. These issues include landfill management, residential waste management, building codes and, in some cases, power generation. They also directly control a significant number of cars and trucks in their municipal fleets.

The Federation of Canadian Municipalities (FCM) has been prominent in its efforts to reduce greenhouse gas emissions under the control of municipal governments. In 1995, the FCM established its "20% Club," of which Ottawa, Toronto, Regina, Edmonton and Vancouver were the founding members. Members have committed to reduce their greenhouse gas emissions by 20 per cent below 1990 levels by 2005.

The 20% Club has since evolved into the *Partners for Climate Protection Program,* a national program that brings Canadian municipal governments together to reduce the local production of greenhouse gas emissions. Members are encouraged to undertake corporate and community-wide greenhouse gas emission inventories and then establish a target of reducing emissions from municipal operations by 20 per cent, and community-wide emissions by a minimum of six per cent, within 10 years of joining. As of February 2003, 106 municipalities were members of Partners for Climate Protection, representing more than 60 per cent of Canada's population. For more information on what the member municipalities are doing across Canada to reduce greenhouse gas emissions, see the program's website at www.fcm.ca/scep/support/PCP/pcp_index.htm. Some notable initiatives from member municipalities are mentioned below:

- **The City of Calgary,** Alberta purchases wind power for its light rail transit system, the "C-Train." The first of its kind in North America, the "Ride the Wind" initiative has been operational since 2001 and reduces CO_2 emissions by 26,000 tonnes every year. As the C-Train lines are extended, the savings in emissions will also increase.

Figure 4-2

Calgary's C-Train

Although Calgary's C-Train itself does not produce CO_2 emissions, the supply of electricity used for C-Train traction power formerly originated from greenhouse gas producing coal or natural gas powered facilities. The C-Train is now 100 per cent emissions free because its fleet is powered by clean wind-generated electricity.

Source: Calgary Transit.

- **The City of Greater Sudbury,** through EarthCare Sudbury, has set a target to locally produce 50 per cent of the energy the city consumes. The City of Greater Sudbury launched a biodiesel pilot project in late July 2003. The city's plan is to produce three million litres of fuel per year at an eco-industrial park located near the city's landfill site. The city also plans to build a wind farm that could produce up to 75 megawatts of electricity – enough to power about 40,000 homes.

- In 1990, **the City of Toronto** made a commitment to reduce the city's net CO_2 emissions by 20 per cent relative to 1988 levels by the year 2005. To help achieve this goal the Better Buildings Partnership (BBP) was launched in 1996. BBP promotes comprehensive energy-efficient retrofits and building renewal initiatives for public and private sector buildings, including commercial, institutional and multi-residential. The BBP's goal is to implement approximately 400 million square feet of energy efficiency retrofits in the city by 2008–2012.

- **The City of Vancouver** and Maxim Power Corporation have developed a project that will use collected landfill gas (produced from the decomposition of waste and largely consisting of two major greenhouse gases, CO_2 and methane) to produce electricity for local greenhouses. The total greenhouse gas emission reductions associated with collecting and beneficially using landfill gas, compared to venting it, is expected to be equivalent to approximately 230,000 tonnes of CO_2 per year, or the emissions of approximately 45,000 automobiles.

Actions Taken by Canadian Industry

More than 930 Canadian businesses and organizations have joined the Voluntary Challenge and Registry (VCR). This government–private sector initiative has encouraged voluntary reductions of emissions of greenhouse gases since 1997. For a full list of member companies along with their action plans, visit www.vcr-mvr.ca. Some notable initiatives set forth by VCR members include the following:

- In 1995, **Enbridge Gas Distribution** launched a comprehensive programme encouraging and enabling customers to use natural gas more efficiently. Projecting to the end of 2003, Enbridge will have helped its customers save approximately 2.5 million tonnes of CO_2 equivalent from being released into the atmosphere. Enbridge has also invested in energy conservation measures in its Toronto offices and buildings. Between 1991 and 2002, it saved 3.68 million kilowatt hours and 368,000 cubic metres of natural gas. These savings represent a reduction of almost 700 tonnes of CO_2 emissions.

Figure 4-3

SunBridge Wind Power Project

Source: www.suncor.com.

- In 2000, **Suncor Energy Inc.** announced plans to invest $100 million by the end of 2005 in renewable energy projects. The first major step in that commitment was the launch of the SunBridge Wind Power Project (a 50/50 partnership between Suncor and Enbridge) in Saskatchewan. This $22 million project is expected to offset 33,000 tonnes of CO_2 per year. Suncor is also investigating means of capturing or offsetting the greenhouse gases that are produced in its operations. For example, as part of the "CO_2 Capture Project," Suncor is working with a coalition of major energy companies to support research into the viability of injecting waste CO_2 into underground storage reservoirs.

- In 1995, **Shell Canada** set out to stabilize, at 1990 levels, the greenhouse gas emissions for its existing businesses by the year 2000. It achieved that target, primarily through the development and implementation of energy efficiency projects, and is now committed to a further six per cent reduction by 2008. In 2001, its greenhouse gas emissions were 76 thousand tonnes less than those in 2000.

- **Noranda Inc.**, a Toronto-based mining and metals company, has reduced its greenhouse gas emissions through process improvement, better capacity utilization, increased recycling, and the development and deployment of innovative new process technologies. Noranda is committed to reduce greenhouse gas emissions intensity by at least one per cent per year at all operations for the period of 2000–2012.

- **Honda of Canada Manufacturing** is committed to reducing greenhouse gas emissions from the energy sources of its manufacturing and assembly operations by five per cent per vehicle produced by the end of 2005, using 2000 as a baseline. Since 2001, Honda has reduced its greenhouse gas emissions per vehicle by 7.5 per cent. Since 1990, greenhouse gas emissions per vehicle have decreased by more than 35 per cent.

Adapting To Climate Change

As we have learned, steps are currently being taken by government and industry to decrease greenhouse gas emissions in the future (known as "mitigation"). However, the effects of climate change are already being experienced around the globe. Therefore, protective actions must also be taken to reduce people's vulnerability to climate change and any consequent impacts. These actions are referred to as "adaptation."

Adaptive measures range from actions by individuals, governments and industries, to policies related to planning and infrastructure development. Actions can be taken at local, national and international scales, and may involve technological, institutional and behavioural changes. In terms of responding to the health effects of climate change, adaptive measures can include improving access to cooler or air-conditioned environments, providing protective shelter and clothing, and improving monitoring of weather conditions (e.g., implementing early weather warnings and advisories, such as severe cold weather alerts, or developing hot weather/health watch systems, such as that of the City of Toronto (see Box 2-5 on page 21)). The re-design of an area's infrastructure is also a common adaptive measure, (e.g., updating a municipality's sewage system to accommodate increased runoff, or constructing floodways and breakwaters to minimize the effects of flooding). Likewise, extending or upgrading existing coastal dyke systems would protect against sea level rise.

While these actions would help Canadians better adapt to the current climate and to anticipated climate change, many research activities are also underway to improve our understanding of the health effects and the adaptive capacity of health infrastructure. In Canada, both the Health Policy Research Program of Health Canada and the Impacts and Adaptation Program of the Government of Canada's Climate Change Action Fund have funded research projects related to climate change and health. Health Canada also has a Climate Change Health Office, which, as part of the Canadian Climate Impacts and Adaptation Research Network, coordinates research activities undertaken by government scientists, university researchers, health professionals and non-governmental organizations. The Adaptation and Impacts Research Group of Environment Canada has also conducted research on various aspects of climate change and health in Canada.

For information on climate change health effects research in Canada, visit the following websites:

Natural Resources Canada:

http://adaptation.nrcan.gc.ca

Canadian Institutes of Health Research:

www.cihr-irsc.gc.ca

Health Canada:

www.hc-sc.gc.ca/hecs-sesc/ccho

Environment Canada:

www.msc-smc.ec.gc.ca/AIRG/index_e.cfm

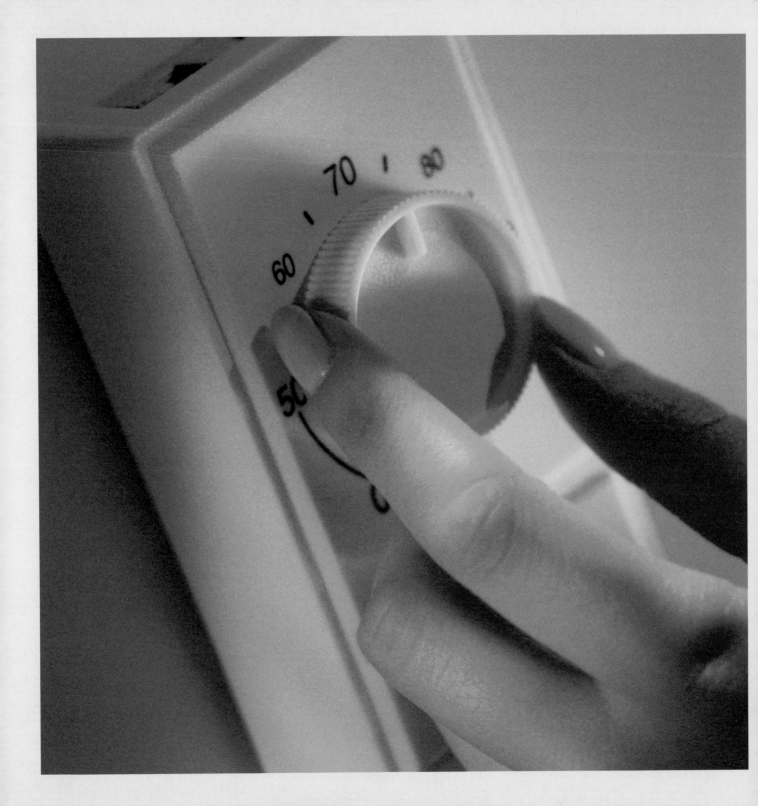

chapter 5

Personal Actions to Reduce Greenhouse Gas Emissions

What You Can Do

In 2001, Canada contributed about 720 megatonnes of greenhouse gases to the atmosphere. Everyday activities by individuals account for more than a quarter of these emissions – that's about five tonnes per person per year. Transportation and heating of homes are major contributors of personal greenhouse gas emissions in Canada (see Figure 5.1).

There are many simple and effective daily actions that can help reduce the amount of greenhouse gases individuals release into the air.

Figure 5-1

Source of Personal Greenhouse Gases in Canada

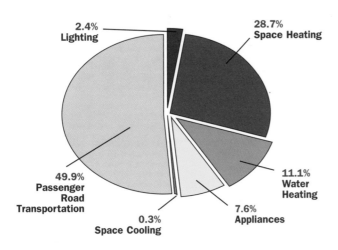

2.4% Lighting

28.7% Space Heating

49.9% Passenger Road Transportation

0.3% Space Cooling

7.6% Appliances

11.1% Water Heating

Source: Environment Canada.

The Government of Canada has launched "The One-Tonne Challenge" which calls on every Canadian to reduce his or her annual greenhouse gas emissions by one tonne, or 20 per cent. For more details, go to www.climatechange.gc.ca.

To start on your one-tonne emission reduction challenge, actions can be taken at home, at work and on the road.

At Home

There are many practical things you can do at home to reduce greenhouse gas emissions. A large portion of emissions from the home come from heating. The higher the heat, the more fossil fuels are being burned at the power plants that supply much of our electricity needs, adding huge quantities of greenhouse gases to the atmosphere. Cooling has an impact as well. Though the energy load of air conditioning is a small part of residential energy use across Canada, it does place seasonal demands on power plants that supply much of our electricity needs (particularly those in Southern Ontario).

WHAT YOU CAN DO	WHY
Draft-proof your house or apartment. Seal all leaks around around doors, windows and cracks where heat may be escaping. Consider purchasing the EnerGuide For Houses service and have an energy expert come to your home to advise you on what needs to be done to make your home more energy-efficient. For more information, go to http://energuideforhouses.gc.ca	**Sealing leaks and drafts around the house can reduce your home's heating needs by up to 20 per cent.**
Install energy efficient windows and doors.	**Windows can account for up to 25 per cent of total house heat loss.**
Clean furnace filters regularly and keep the furnace properly tuned.	**A well-maintained unit uses 10 to 15 per cent less energy than a poorly maintained one.**
Conserve hot water by shortening showers and using the cold or warm wash and rinse in the washing machine.	**Energy consumption for water heating is one of the largest uses in the home, second only to the furnace for space heating.**
Properly insulate your house.	**Poorly insulated homes allow heat to flow through the exterior walls, floors or roof, forcing the furnace to use more energy to keep the house warm.**
Turn off lights, appliances, televisions and computers when they're not being used. Whenever possible use a small appliance instead of a large one (e.g., use a toaster oven in place of a full-sized oven).	**Consuming energy when it's not needed is wasteful and costs money.**
Major household appliances can consume up to 16 per cent of the total energy used in the home. Check the "EnerGuide" label when buying new appliances or room air conditioners.	**The EnerGuide label — affixed to most household major appliances and room air conditioners — shows how much energy your appliances consume in a year of normal service. You are then able to compare the energy efficiency of each model to others of the same size and class.**

WHAT YOU CAN DO	WHY
Install a programmable thermostat to automatically lower the temperature of your home when at work during the day, and at night when asleep.	**For every degree you lower your thermostat, you'll save two per cent on your heating bill. A reduction of 3˚C at night when you are asleep or during the day when you are not at home, provides optimal savings.**
Use energy-efficient lighting products, such as compact fluorescent bulbs.	**They last 10 times longer and use 75 per cent less energy than regular bulbs.**
Install low-flow showerheads and toilets.	**Low-flow showerheads use up to 60 per cent less water than conventional showerheads. Low-flow toilets use about 7.3 litres of water per flush, while traditional toilets can use 14 to 23 litres per flush.**
Fix leaky faucets immediately.	**At one drop per second, a single leaky washer wastes the equivalent of 16 baths every month.**
Purchase "green power" to meet your home's electricity needs. Contact your power supplier to see where and if it is available.	**Green power is energy that is generated from low-impact renewable sources, such as water, solar energy and wind. Green power emits little or no greenhouse gases.**
Reduce your home's cooling needs. Set your air conditioner at 24˚C and raise it when you go out.	**For each degree set below 24˚C, you use three to five per cent more energy.**

At Work

Canadians spend a good part of their day in the workplace. There are many opportunities to reduce greenhouse gas emissions at work.

WHAT YOU CAN DO	WHY
Ask your employer to join Pollution Probe's S-M-A-R-T Movement program (Save Money and the Air by Reducing Trips). For more information, see www.pollutionprobe.org/whatwedo/Smart.htm.	Carpooling, teleworking and active commuting can lead to substantial reductions in greenhouse gases. In fact, if you drive 20,000 kilometres a year, driving 10 per cent less will reduce your greenhouse gas emissions by half a tonne.
Use as little paper as possible. Conserve by printing and copying on both sides. File e-mails on your computer rather than printing them out.	Pulp and papermaking is the fifth largest industrial consumer of energy in the world, using as much power to produce a tonne of product as the iron and steel industry. In addition to saving energy, by reducing the amount of paper we use more trees will remain in the forests where they are able to remove some of the excess CO_2 from the atmosphere.
Make sure computers, printers and photocopiers are all switched off before leaving the workplace.	These machines can use a lot of your workplace's energy. Less energy use means fewer greenhouse gas emissions.
Avoid using a laser printer when printing draft documents.	From an energy use perspective, the order of preference is ink-jet, dot matrix and laser.

On the Road

The transportation sector is the single largest producer of greenhouse gas emissions in Canada. The average car produces about three times its weight in CO_2 every year. Cars that are poorly driven and poorly maintained produce even more CO_2. Here are some suggestions on how to be more aware of your greenhouse gas emissions when you have to get someplace.

WHAT YOU CAN DO	WHY
Use public transportation instead of the car (if you own one). Carpool, walk or ride your bicycle.	**One busload of passengers takes 40 vehicles off the road during rush hour, saves 70,000 litres of fuel and avoids more than 175 tonnes of greenhouse gas emissions a year. Carpooling with one other person immediately halves the greenhouse gas emissions for that trip. On average, a carpool saves 2,000 litres of gasoline a year.**
Consider fuel efficiency when purchasing a vehicle, and keep vehicles well maintained. Check out the Personal Vehicles Website (www.oee.nrcan.gc.ca/vehicles) to find out which vehicles are most fuel-efficient.	**A large car that burns 14 litres of gasoline to travel 100 kilometres will emit 66 tonnes of CO_2 during its lifetime (assuming 20,000 kilometres driven a year for 10 years). A typical smaller car that burns nine litres every 100 kilometres will emit only 42 tonnes of CO_2 over the same total distance. By choosing the more fuel-efficient car, you can save 24 tonnes of CO_2 from being emitted.**
Keep all vehicles fully tuned.	**A poorly maintained vehicle can produce 50 per cent more CO_2 than one that runs properly.**
Avoid idling your vehicle. If stopping for 10 seconds or more, except in traffic, turn the car engine off.	**According to Natural Resources Canada's Office of Energy Efficiency, idling an average car for 10 minutes every day can produce approximately a quarter tonne of CO_2 emissions each year.**
Keep to the speed limit. On the highway, use cruise control to maintain a steady speed and reduce fuel consumption.	**Increasing your highway cruising speed from 100 km/h to 120 km/h will increase fuel consumption by 20 per cent.**
Check your vehicle's tire pressure once a month.	**Inflated tires cut down on "drag," thereby saving on fuel and harmful emissions. By keeping your vehicle's tires properly inflated, you could reduce CO_2 emissions by at least 0.16 tonne each year.**

References

Canadian Council of Ministers of the Environment. 2003. *Climate, Nature, People: Indicators of Canada's Changing Climate.* Winnipeg: CCME.

Environment Canada. 2002. *Frequently Asked Questions about the Science of Climate Change.* Science Assessment and Policy Integration Branch. Ottawa: Environment Canada.

Environment Canada. 1998. *The Canada Country Study: Climate Impacts and Adaptation.* Ottawa: Environment Canada.

Epstein, Paul. 2000. *"Is Global Warming Harmful to Health?"* Scientific American, August 2000.

Government of Canada. 2002. *Climate Change Plan for Canada.* Ottawa: Government of Canada.

IPCC. 2001. *Climate Change 2001: Synthesis Report. A Contribution of Working Groups I, II, and III to the Third Assessment Report of the Intergovernmental Panel on Climate Change.* Watson, R.T. and the Core Writing Team (eds.). Cambridge, UK and New York, NY: Cambridge University Press.

National Institutes of Health. 2001. *Environmental Health Perspectives Supplements: Climate Change and Human Health.* Volume 109, Number S2, May 2001.

Natural Resources Canada. 2002. *Climate Change Impacts and Adaptation: A Canadian Perspective.* Prepared by the Climate Change Impacts and Adaptation Directorate. Ottawa: Natural Resources Canada.

Pembina Institute. 2000. *A Climate Change Resource Book for Journalists.* First Edition. Drayton Valley, AB: Pembina Institute.

Pollution Probe. 2002. *Towards an Adaptation Action Plan: Climate Change and Health in the Toronto–Niagara Region – Technical Report.* Toronto: Pollution Probe.

World Health Organization. 2003. *Climate Change and Human Health – Risks and Responses – Summary.* Geneva: World Health Organization.

World Health Organization. 2000. *Climate Change and Human Health: Impact and Adaptation.* Geneva: World Health Organization.

Useful Websites

To learn more about climate change, visit the following websites:

Government

Canadian Climate Impacts and Adaptation Research Network: www.c-ciarn.ca

Environment Canada Climate Change: www.ec.gc.ca/climate/home-e.html

Government of Canada Climate Change: www.climatechange.gc.ca

Health Canada – Climate Change and Health Office: www.hc-sc.gc.ca/hecs-sesc/ccho

Intergovernmental Panel on Climate Change (IPCC): www.ipcc.ch

Natural Resources Canada – Climate Change Impacts and Adaptation: http://adaptation.nrcan.gc.ca

Natural Resources Canada – Office of Energy Efficiency: www.oee.nrcan.gc.ca

United States Environmental Protection Agency: www.epa.gov/globalwarming

Non-governmental

Climate Action Network (CANet) – A network of more than 100 organizations across Canada committed to preventing dangerous levels of human interference with the global climate system: www.climateactionnetwork.ca

Climatechangesolutions.com – A project of the Pembina Institute that offers interactive tools, resources and success stories on actions to reduce greenhouse gas emissions: www.climatechangesolutions.com

Encyclopedia of the Atmospheric Environment – An on-line encyclopedia, for both younger and older users, that discusses a range of atmospheric issues, including global warming and ozone depletion: www.doc.mmu.ac.uk/aric/eae/english.html

International Institute for Sustainable Development (Observations of Climate Change): http://iisd.ca/climatechange.htm

Sierra Club of Canada – Climate Change, Energy and Atmosphere Programme: www.sierraclub.ca

Union of Concerned Scientists – Citizens and Scientists for Environmental Solutions: www.ucsusa.org/global_environment/global_warming/index.cfm